Additional Practice

▶ Topics 1–15

MATHEMATICS

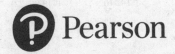

Glenview, Illinois   Boston, Massachusetts
Chandler, Arizona   New York, New York

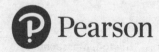

ISBN-13:   978-0-13-491221-9
ISBN-10:   0-13-491221-7

4 19

Grade 1 Topics 1–15

Topic 1
Understand Addition and Subtraction

Lesson 1-1 1
Lesson 1-2 3
Lesson 1-3 5
Lesson 1-4 7
Lesson 1-5 9
Lesson 1-6 11
Lesson 1-7 13
Lesson 1-8 15
Lesson 1-9 17

Topic 2
Fluently Add and Subtract Within 10

Lesson 2-1 19
Lesson 2-2 21
Lesson 2-3 23
Lesson 2-4 25
Lesson 2-5 27
Lesson 2-6 29
Lesson 2-7 31
Lesson 2-8 33
Lesson 2-9 35

Topic 3
Addition Facts to 20: Use Strategies

Lesson 3-1 37
Lesson 3-2 39

Lesson 3-3 41
Lesson 3-4 43
Lesson 3-5 45
Lesson 3-6 47
Lesson 3-7 49
Lesson 3-8 51
Lesson 3-9 53

Topic 4
Subtraction Facts to 20: Use Strategies

Lesson 4-1 55
Lesson 4-2 57
Lesson 4-3 59
Lesson 4-4 61
Lesson 4-5 63
Lesson 4-6 65
Lesson 4-7 67
Lesson 4-8 69
Lesson 4-9 71

Topic 5
Work with Addition and Subtraction Equations

Lesson 5-1 73
Lesson 5-2 75
Lesson 5-3 77
Lesson 5-4 79
Lesson 5-5 81
Lesson 5-6 83
Lesson 5-7 85

Topic 6
Represent and Interpret Data

Lesson 6-1 87
Lesson 6-2 89
Lesson 6-3 91
Lesson 6-4 93
Lesson 6-5 95

Topic 7
Extend the Counting Sequence

Lesson 7-1 97
Lesson 7-2 99
Lesson 7-3 101
Lesson 7-4 103
Lesson 7-5 105
Lesson 7-6 107
Lesson 7-7 109

Topic 8
Understand Place Value

Lesson 8-1 111
Lesson 8-2 113
Lesson 8-3 115
Lesson 8-4 117
Lesson 8-5 119
Lesson 8-6 121
Lesson 8-7 123

Topic 9
Compare Two-Digit Numbers

Lesson 9-1 125
Lesson 9-2 127
Lesson 9-3 129
Lesson 9-4 131
Lesson 9-5 133
Lesson 9-6 135

Topic 10
Use Models and Strategies to Add Tens and Ones

Lesson 10-1 137
Lesson 10-2 139
Lesson 10-3 141
Lesson 10-4 143
Lesson 10-5 145
Lesson 10-6 147
Lesson 10-7 149
Lesson 10-8 151
Lesson 10-9 153

Topic 11
Use Models and Strategies to Subtract Tens

Lesson 11-1 155
Lesson 11-2 157
Lesson 11-3 159
Lesson 11-4 161
Lesson 11-5 163
Lesson 11-6 165
Lesson 11-7 167

Topic 12
Measure Lengths

Lesson 12-1 169
Lesson 12-2 171
Lesson 12-3 173
Lesson 12-4 175

Topic 13
Time and Money

Lesson 13-1 177
Lesson 13-2 179
Lesson 13-3 181
Lesson 13-4 183
Lesson 13-5 185
Lesson 13-6 187

Topic 14
Reason with Shapes and Their Attributes

Lesson 14-1 189
Lesson 14-2 191
Lesson 14-3 193
Lesson 14-4 195
Lesson 14-5 197
Lesson 14-6 199
Lesson 14-7 201
Lesson 14-8 203
Lesson 14-9 205

Topic 15
Equal Shares of Circles and Rectangles

Lesson 15-1 207
Lesson 15-2 209
Lesson 15-3 211
Lesson 15-4 213

Name _____

Additional Practice 1-1
Add To

Another Look!

Solve. Use color tiles to help.

5 rabbits   3 rabbits join.

I can use color tiles to show rabbits.

How many rabbits now?

■■■■■ ■■■ $\underline{5} + \underline{3} = \underline{8}$ rabbits

HOME ACTIVITY Gather 9 pennies. Tell your child this story: "6 pennies are in a jar. I put 3 more pennies in the jar. How many pennies are there now?" Have your child write the sum.

Solve. Use color tiles to help.

1. 3 frogs   3 frogs join.

How many frogs now?

$\underline{3} + \underline{3} = \underline{6}$ frogs

2. 2 bugs   3 bugs join.

How many bugs now?

___ ◯ ___ ◯ ___ bugs

3. Model

2 dogs

4 dogs join.

How many dogs now?

____ ◯ ____ ◯ ____ dogs

4. Model

5 mice

5 mice join.

How many mice now?

____ ◯ ____ ◯ ____ mice

5. Higher Order Thinking

Write an addition story about the frogs.

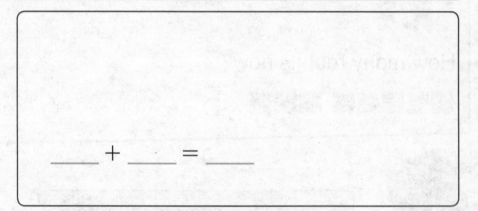

____ + ____ = ____

6. Number Sense

2 hats with dots

2 hats with stripes

How many hats in all?

____ hats

7. 🐊 Assessment Practice

3 ducks   2 ducks join.

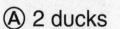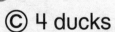

How many ducks now?   🐊 1.OA.1.1

Ⓐ 2 ducks   Ⓒ 4 ducks

Ⓑ 3 ducks   Ⓓ 5 ducks

Name _____

Another Look!

I have 2 dogs and 3 cats. How many pets in all?

Show the parts on a mat.

part   part

Write an addition equation.

$$2 + 3 = 5 \text{ pets}$$

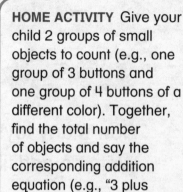

HOME ACTIVITY Give your child 2 groups of small objects to count (e.g., one group of 3 buttons and one group of 4 buttons of a different color). Together, find the total number of objects and say the corresponding addition equation (e.g., "3 plus 4 equals 7."). Repeat the activity several times with different groupings.

Solve. Use counters to help. Write an addition equation.

1. 4 apples and 2 oranges

   How many pieces of fruit in all?

   $$4 + 2 = 6 \text{ pieces of fruit}$$

2. 4 roses and 4 daisies

   How many flowers in all?

   ___ ◯ ___ ◯ ___ flowers

Solve. Use counters to help.

3. Model

3 toy cars and 5 toy trucks

How many toys in all?

Write an addition equation.

_____ ◯ _____ ◯ _____ toys

4. Model

2 big fish and 4 small fish

How many fish in all?

Write an addition equation.

_____ ◯ _____ ◯ _____ fish

5. Higher Order Thinking

5 bananas

4 oranges

2 bananas

How many bananas in all?

Write an addition equation.

_____ ◯ _____ ◯ _____ bananas

6. Assessment Practice

4 ducks and 6 rabbits

How many animals in all? I.OA.I.I

Ⓐ 4 + 4 = 8 animals

Ⓑ 4 + 5 = 9 animals

Ⓒ 2 + 7 = 9 animals

Ⓓ 4 + 6 = 10 animals

Practice Video Tools Games

Another Look!

4 flowers in all

There are always 4 flowers!

Some are inside the vase. Some are outside.
What are some ways?

3 inside
1 outside

2 inside
2 outside

1 inside
3 outside

$$4 = 3 + 1 \qquad 4 = 2 + 2 \qquad 4 = 1 + 3$$

HOME ACTIVITY Give your child the following problem: "Dustin finds 8 leaves. Some are green. The rest are yellow. Write an addition equation to show the numbers of green and yellow leaves." Work with your child to choose parts of 8 and write an equation. Then repeat, choosing different parts of 8.

Use cubes or draw a picture.
Then write an equation.

1. 9 frogs in all
Some are in the water.
Some are in the grass.
Show one way.

____ = ____ + ____

2. Model

8 frogs in all

Some are in the water.

Some are in the grass.

Show one way.

Write an equation.

Use cubes or draw a picture.

___ ◯ ___ ◯ ___

3. Higher Order Thinking

Laura has 7 apples.

She eats 1, 2, or 3 apples.

How many apples could be left?

Tell how you know.

4. Assessment Practice

6 puppies in all

Some puppies have spots.

Some puppies do not have spots.

Which shows one way? 🔘 1.OA.1.1

Ⓐ 2 have spots, 3 do not

Ⓑ 3 have spots, 4 do not

Ⓒ 4 have spots, 2 do not

Ⓓ 5 have spots, 3 do not

Name _____

Another Look! You can subtract to find the difference.

There are 6 cats.

3 cats jump off.

How many cats are left?

$6 - 3 = 3$ cats

There are 5 cats.

2 cats jump off.

How many cats are left?

$5 - 2 = 3$ cats

HOME ACTIVITY Place 8 small objects, such as buttons, on the table. Take away several of the buttons. Ask your child to tell a subtraction story. Then have your child write a subtraction equation to match the story, such as $8 - 2 = 6$. Have your child count the buttons that are left to check if his or her answer is correct.

Solve each problem.
Write a subtraction equation.

1. There are 9 apples.

   7 apples are eaten.

   How many apples are left?

   ___ ___ ___ apples

2. There are 10 crayons.

   7 crayons fall out.

   How many crayons are left?

   ___ ◯ ___ ◯ ___ crayons

3. Reasoning

There are 6 bees.

4 bees fly away.

How many bees are left?

____ ◯ ____ ◯ ____ bees

4. Reasoning

There are 8 ducks.

4 ducks get out.

How many ducks are left?

____ ◯ ____ ◯ ____ ducks

5. Higher Order Thinking

Find the missing number.

Then write a subtraction story.

Use pictures, words, or numbers.

$$7 - 3 = \underline{\quad}$$

6. **Assessment Practice**

There are 10 balloons.

2 balloons pop.

How many balloons are left?

1.OA.1.1

Ⓐ $9 - 4 = 5$ balloons

Ⓑ $10 - 3 = 7$ balloons

Ⓒ $8 - 1 = 7$ balloons

Ⓓ $10 - 2 = 8$ balloons

Name _____

Another Look!

You can use cubes to **compare**.

You can subtract to find how many **more**.

You can count to help subtract.

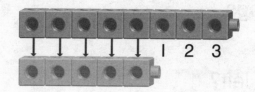 1 2 3

How many gray cubes? __8__

How many white cubes? __5__

Write an equation. __8__ – __5__ = __3__

How many more gray cubes? __3__

HOME ACTIVITY Give your child 5 blue buttons and 2 green buttons. Ask: Are there more blue or green buttons? Have your child tell how many more blue buttons than green buttons he or she has. Repeat with up to 10 blue buttons and 10 green buttons.

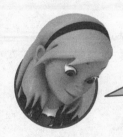 Complete each problem.
Write a subtraction equation to match.

1.  ____ gray cubes
____ white cubes

Which color has more cubes? _____

How many more? ____

Equation: ____ ____ ____

2.  ____ white cubes
____ gray cube

Which color has more cubes? _____

How many more? ____

Equation: ____ ◯ ____ ◯ ____

3. Number Sense

Sam plays with 5 dogs.

3 dogs go home.

How many dogs are left?

____ ◯ ____ ◯ ____

____ dogs

4. Model

David has 6 tickets.

Mimi has 2 tickets.

How many more tickets does David have than Mimi?

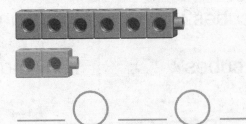

____ ◯ ____ ◯ ____

____ more tickets

5. Higher Order Thinking

Draw some red cubes.

Draw more blue cubes than red cubes.

Write a subtraction equation.

____ – ____ = ____ more blue cubes

6. Assessment Practice

Lucy has 6 apples.

Julie has 7 apples.

How many more apples does Julie have than Lucy? I.OA.I.I

Ⓐ 0 more apples

Ⓑ I more apple

Ⓒ 6 more apples

Ⓓ 7 more apples

Use cubes or draw a picture.

Name _____

Another Look!

You can use cubes to **compare**.

You can subtract to find how many **fewer**.

You can count to help subtract.

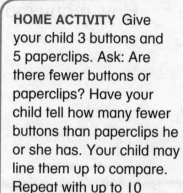

1 2 3 4 5

How many gray cubes? __3__

How many white cubes? __8__

Write an equation. __8__ - __3__ = __5__

How many fewer gray cubes? __5__

HOME ACTIVITY Give your child 3 buttons and 5 paperclips. Ask: Are there fewer buttons or paperclips? Have your child tell how many fewer buttons than paperclips he or she has. Your child may line them up to compare. Repeat with up to 10 buttons and 10 paperclips.

Complete each problem.
Write a subtraction equation to match.

1. 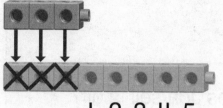 ____ gray cubes

____ white cubes

Which color has fewer cubes? _____

How many fewer? ____

____ ____ ____

2.  ____ gray cubes

____ white cubes

Which color has fewer cubes? _____

How many fewer? ____

____ ◯ ____ ◯ ____

3. Reasoning

Jan sells 5 muffins.

Then she sells 2 more.

How many muffins does Jan sell in all?

___ ◯ ___ ◯ ___

___ muffins

4. Reasoning

There are 6 butterflies.

3 butterflies fly away.

How many butterflies are left?

___ ◯ ___ ◯ ___

___ butterflies

5. Higher Order Thinking

Draw some red cubes.
Draw fewer green cubes.
Write an equation to match your drawing.

___ − ___ = ___ fewer green cubes

6. **Assessment Practice**

10 cats

6 dogs

How many fewer dogs than cats are there? I.OA.I.I

Ⓐ 8 fewer dogs

Ⓑ 6 fewer dogs

Ⓒ 4 fewer dogs

Ⓓ 2 fewer dogs

Use cubes or draw a picture.

Name _____

Another Look!

Jim has 4 golf balls.

He finds more golf balls.

Now Jim has 7 golf balls.

How many golf balls did Jim find?

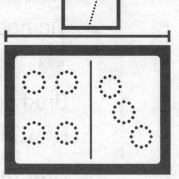

$$\underline{4} + \underline{3} = \underline{7}$$

_____ golf balls

Solve. Complete the model.
Write an equation.

1. 2 cats play.

More cats join them.

Now there are 7 cats playing.

How many cats joined?

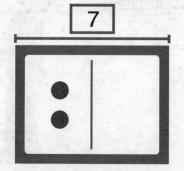

7

_____ + _____ = _____

_____ cats

2. 8 friends are eating.

More friends join them.

Now there are 10 friends eating.

How many friends joined?

10

_____ ◯ _____ ◯ _____

_____ friends

3. Model

Linda has 4 lemons.

She buys 4 more lemons.

How many lemons does Linda have now?

___ ◯ ___ ◯ ___

___ lemons

4. Model

Tia has 5 berries.

Brad gives her more berries.

Now Tia has 9 berries.

How many berries did Brad give Tia?

___ ◯ ___ ◯ ___

___ berries

5. Higher Order Thinking

Complete the equation.
Then write a story to match
the equation.

$$8 + \underline{\quad} = 10$$

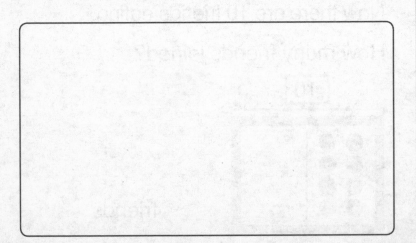

6. ⏵ Assessment Practice

Ria has 7 coins.
Gary gives her more coins.
Now Ria has 10 coins.

How many coins did Gary give Ria? Ⓣ I.OA.I.I

Ⓐ 2 coins

Ⓑ 3 coins

Ⓒ 4 coins

Ⓓ 5 coins

You can use cubes or draw a picture.

Name _____

 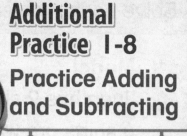

Additional Practice 1-8
Practice Adding and Subtracting

Another Look!

The dog has 8 spots.

6 spots are white.

The rest are black.

How many spots are black?

You can subtract or add to solve.

$$8 - 6 = 2$$

spots in all — white spots — black spots

$$6 + 2 = 8$$

white spots + black spots = spots in all

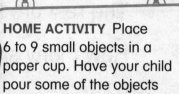

HOME ACTIVITY Place 6 to 9 small objects in a paper cup. Have your child pour some of the objects onto the table. Ask, "How many are still in the cup?" Have your child subtract the number of objects on the table from the number he or she started with. Then have your child count the objects that are left to check if his or her answer is correct.

Each dog has black and brown spots.
Draw the missing brown spots.
Write an equation and solve.

1. 6 spots in all

____ ◯ ____ ◯ ____

____ brown spots

2. 9 spots in all

____ ◯ ____ ◯ ____

____ brown spots

3. 7 spots in all

____ ◯ ____ ◯ ____

____ brown spots

4. **Model**

Juan has 9 shirts.

6 shirts are white.

The rest are **NOT** white.

How many shirts are **NOT** white?

Write an equation. Then solve.

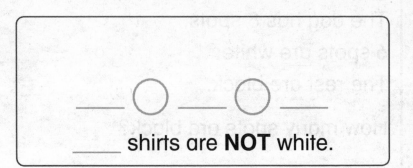

_____ shirts are **NOT** white.

5. **Higher Order Thinking**

Draw pictures and write the missing numbers.

Number of Fruit	Drawings	🍌 Bananas	🍊 Oranges
8 in all		4	___
6 in all		___	2

6. **Assessment Practice**

Pedro and Deb have 9 baseball cards in all.

Deb has 1 baseball card.

How many baseball cards does Pedro have?

Which equation matches the story? 🌀 I.OA.I.I

(A) $9 - 1 = 8$ baseball cards

(B) $8 - 1 = 7$ baseball cards

(C) $8 - 7 = 1$ baseball card

(D) $7 - 1 = 6$ baseball cards

Name _____

Another Look! Explain how you solve the problem.

Bill has 6 bananas.

He keeps 1 banana.

He gives the rest away.

How many bananas does he give away?

Solve and explain.

KEEP 1

5 $6 - 1 = 5$ GIVE

I drew a picture and used numbers.

Solve. Use pictures, numbers, or words to explain.

1. Tim has 7 toy cars.

   He buys 2 more cars.

   How many cars does Tim have now?

Seashells

Karen and Kai go to the beach.
They find seashells.
Solve each problem.
Show how you know.

Use pictures, words, or numbers to show your work.

2. Explain

Karen finds 5 seashells.

Kai finds 3 seashells.

How many seashells in all? 1.OA.1.1, MP.3.1

3. Be Precise

Who finds more seashells, Karen or Kai?

How many more? 1.OA.1.1, MP.6.1

Name **Sophie**

Another Look! Count on to find each sum.

Add 1.
The sum is 1 more.

3, 4

$3 + 1 = 4$

Add 2.
The sum is 2 more.

3, 4, 5

$3 + 2 = \underline{5}$

Add 3.
The sum is 3 more.

3, 4, 5, 6

$3 + 3 = \underline{6}$

HOME ACTIVITY Place between 1 and 7 small objects on a table. Have your child count the objects. Then place 1, 2, or 3 more. Ask your child to add the objects. Have your child write an addition equation to correspond with the objects on the table. Repeat with a different number of objects.

Count on to complete the addition facts.

1.

6, $\underline{1}$

$6 + 1 = \underline{7}$

2.

5, $\underline{3}$, $\underline{}$, $\underline{}$

$5 + 3 = \underline{8}$

3.

7, $\underline{2}$, $\underline{}$

$7 + 2 = \underline{9}$

4. Max earns 5 dollars.

Then he earns some more dollars.

In all, Max earns 7 dollars.

How many more dollars did Max earn?

Draw a picture. Write the number.

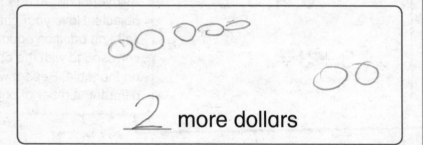

_2_ more dollars

5. Emma reads 7 books.

Then she reads 3 more books.

How many books did Emma read in all?

Draw a picture. Write the number.

_10_ books

6. Higher Order Thinking

Write the missing number.

$3 + 2 = 2 + 3$

Use the picture to help!

7. 🔲 **Assessment Practice**

Which is the sum for $6 + 3$? I.OA.3.5

Ⓐ 3

Ⓑ 6

Ⓒ 8

Ⓓ 9

You can count on to help add.

Practice   Video   Tools   Games

Another Look!

A doubles fact has the same addends.
Here are some doubles facts.

$$2 \\ +2 \\ \overline{4}$$

$$2 + 2 = 4$$

addend   addend   sum

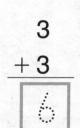

$$3 \\ +3 \\ \boxed{6}$$

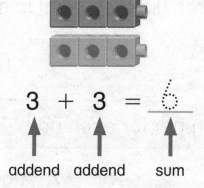

$$3 + 3 = \underline{6}$$

addend   addend   sum

Additional Practice 2-2
Doubles

HOME ACTIVITY Have your child use small objects to show 2 groups of 4. Then ask your child to write an addition equation to show the double $(4 + 4 = 8)$. Repeat for other doubles of $1 + 1$ through $5 + 5$.

Write the sum for each doubles fact.

1.

$$1 \\ +1 \\ \boxed{}$$

2.

$$4 \\ +4 \\ \boxed{}$$

3.

$$5 \\ +5 \\ \boxed{}$$

4. Reasoning

Owen paints 5 pictures.

Luis paints 5 pictures, too.

How many pictures did they paint in all?

_____ pictures

5. Reasoning

Tess and Maya grow 6 flowers in all.

Tess grows 3 flowers.

How many flowers does Maya grow?

_____ flowers

Write the missing number for each problem.

6. Algebra

$4 = 2 +$ _____

7. Algebra

_____ $+ 4 = 8$

8. Algebra

$0 +$ _____ $= 0$

9. Higher Order Thinking

There are 6 marbles in all.

How many marbles are inside the cup?

_____ marbles are inside the cup.

10. 🔊 **Assessment Practice**

Which doubles fact has a sum

of 10? 🔊 I.OA.3.6

Ⓐ $5 + 5$

Ⓑ $5 + 6$

Ⓒ $6 + 5$

Ⓓ $6 + 6$

Name _____

Additional Practice 2-3
Near Doubles

Another Look! You can use doubles to add near doubles.

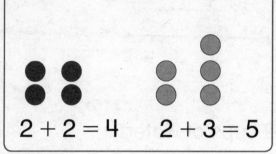

$2 + 2 = 4$ $2 + 3 = 5$

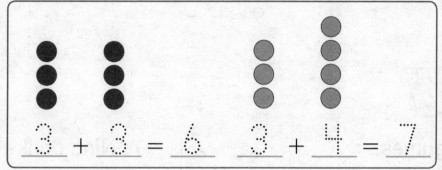

$3 + 3 = 6$ $3 + 4 = 7$

$2 + 2 = 4$
$2 + 3$ is 1 more.
So, $2 + 3 = 5$

$3 + 3 = 6$
$3 + 4$ is 1 more.
So, $3 + 4 = 7$

HOME ACTIVITY Play a game with small objects, like pennies. First, use the pennies to represent numbers that are doubles. Ask your child to add the set of doubles. Then add another penny and ask your child to add the set of near doubles.

Add the doubles.
Then add the near doubles.

1.

___ + ___ = ___   ___ + ___ = ___

2.

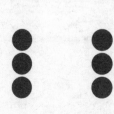

___ + ___ = ___   ___ + ___ = ___

Complete each near doubles fact.

3. Algebra

$3 + \underline{} = 7$

4. Algebra

$9 = 4 + \underline{}$

5. Algebra

$1 + \underline{} = 4$

Solve each problem.

6. Sandy plays 3 games.
Bill plays 3 games and then 1 more.
How many games do they play in all?

____ games

7. Nina drinks 2 cups of water.
Karen drinks 4 cups of water.
How many cups do they drink in all?

____ cups

8. Higher Order Thinking
Use each card once.
Write two addition equations using
doubles and near doubles.

$\underline{} + \underline{} = \underline{}$

$\underline{} + \underline{} = \underline{}$

9. Assessment Practice
Which doubles fact can help you
solve $4 + 5 = ?$ I.OA.3.5

Ⓐ $1 + 1 = 2$

Ⓑ $2 + 2 = 4$

Ⓒ $3 + 3 = 6$

Ⓓ $4 + 4 = 8$

You can count on to help add.

Name _____

Another Look!

You can write an addition fact with 5 using a ten-frame.

You can also write an addition fact for 10 using a ten-frame.

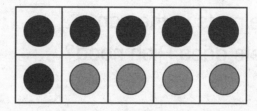

$5 + 1 = 6$

$6 + 4 = \underline{10}$

HOME ACTIVITY Play a game using ten-frames drawn on a sheet of paper. Draw circles on each ten-frame. Then ask your child to write an accompanying equation using 5 or 10 below each ten-frame.

Look at the ten-frames.

Write an addition fact with 5.

Then write an addition fact for 10.

I.

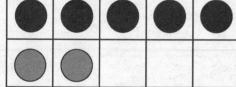

$5 + 2 = \underline{}$

$\underline{} + \underline{} = 10$

2.

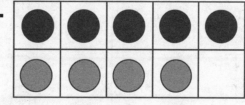

$5 + 4 = \underline{}$

$\underline{} + \underline{} = 10$

3.

$5 + 0 = \underline{}$

$\underline{} + \underline{} = 10$

4. 5 + ___ = ___

6 + ___ = 10

5. 5 + ___ = ___

9 + ___ = 10

6. 5 + ___ = ___

8 + ___ = 10

7. enVision® STEM Rich needs 10 helmets for safety. He puts 4 helmets in the van. How many more helmets does Rich need?

Draw counters to solve.
Then write an equation and solve.

___ + ___ = ___   ___ helmets

8. Higher Order Thinking A box has 7 fruits in all. 5 are peaches. The rest are oranges. How many oranges?

Draw counters to solve.
Then write an equation and solve.

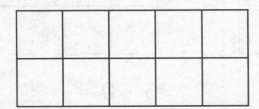

___ = ___ + ___   ___ oranges

9. **Assessment Practice**

Which sums equal 10?
Choose three that apply. ● I.OA.3.6

☐ 6 + 3 = ___

☐ 6 + 4 = ___

☐ 2 + 8 = ___

☐ 4 + 6 = ___

Name _____

Another Look! When you change the order of addends, the sum is the same.

4   +   2   =   6

2   +   4   =   6

HOME ACTIVITY Write several addition equations for your child. Have him or her change the order of addends and write the new addition equation. Ask, "How are the addition equations the same? How are they different?"

5   +   2   =   7

2   +   5   =   7

Write addition equations with addends in a different order.

I.

___ + ___ = ___

___ + ___ = ___

2.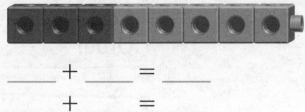

___ + ___ = ___

___ + ___ = ___

3.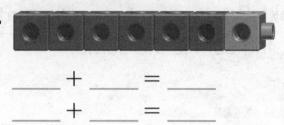

___ + ___ = ___

___ + ___ = ___

4. Higher Order Thinking

Pick two colors of cubes below.

Write an addition story.

Write two addition equations for your story.

___ + ___ = ___

___ + ___ = ___

5. 🔽 **Assessment Practice**

Which shows two ways to add the cubes?

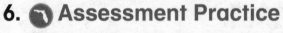 🔽 I.OA.2.3

(A) 4 + 3 and 3 + 4

(B) 2 + 6 and 6 + 2

(C) 2 + 7 and 7 + 2

(D) 5 + 2 and 2 + 5

6. 🔽 **Assessment Practice**

Which has the same sum as 5 + 1?

🔽 I.OA.2.3

(A) 1 + 2

(B) 5 + 3

(C) 2 + 6

(D) 1 + 5

Name _____

Another Look! You can count back to solve subtraction problems.

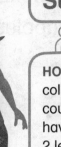

$$0 \quad 1 \quad 2 \quad 3 \quad 4 \quad 5 \quad 6 \quad 7 \quad 8 \quad 9 \quad 10$$

$4 - 2 = ?$

Start at 4.

Count back 2.   **4**, 3, 2

Solve the problem.

$4 - 2 = 2$

$6 - 1 = ?$

Start at 6.

Count back 1.   **6,** _5_

Solve the problem.

$6 - 1 = \underline{5}$

Count back to subtract.

HOME ACTIVITY Using a collection of objects such as counters, count out 6. Then have your child tell what 2 less than 6 equals. Ask, "What subtraction equation did you make?" Continue with other subtraction facts, having your child subtract 0, 1, or 2.

Count back or use a number line to help you subtract.

1.

9

Count back 1.   Solve the problem.

___ $9 - 1 = $ ___

2.

10

Count back 0.   Solve the problem.

___ $10 - 0 = $ ___

Topic 2 | Lesson 6

Go Online | PearsonRealize.com

3. Maya has 8 apples.
She eats 1 apple.
How many apples are left?

_____ − _____ = _____ apples

4. 6 cups sit on a tray.
4 cups fall off.
How many cups are left?

_____ − _____ = _____ cups

5. Higher Order Thinking
Write a subtraction equation.
Then write a story to match
your equation.

You can use pictures, numbers, or words.

_____ _____ = _____ − _____

6. 🐦 **Assessment Practice**
Find 8 − 3. 🐦 1.OA.3.5

Ⓐ 3   Ⓒ 5

Ⓑ 4   Ⓓ 6

0 1 2 3 4 5 6 7 8 9 10

Practice Video Tools Games

Another Look! Use addition to help you subtract.

I know that
2 + 6 = 8.
So, 8 − 6 = 2.

$3 + 6 = 9$

So, $9 - 6 = 3$.

HOME ACTIVITY Fold a sheet of paper in half so you have 2 equal boxes. Put 1–8 pennies in the box on the left. Say a number greater than the number of pennies in the box, but not greater than 9. Ask: "What subtraction equation can you write? What addition equation is related?" Continue with different number combinations.

Write an addition fact that will help you write and solve the subtraction fact.

1.

___ + ___ = ___

So, ___ − ___ = ___.

2.

___ + ___ = ___

So, ___ − ___ = ___.

3.

___ + ___ = ___

So, ___ − ___ = ___.

Solve each problem.

4. Draw the missing counters.
Then write two equations to match.

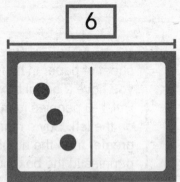

6

_____ − _____ = _____

_____ + _____ = _____

5. Reasoning

Rosi buys 10 beads.

3 of the beads are blue.
The rest are white.

How many white beads does Rosi buy?

_____ white beads

Higher Order Thinking
Draw the shapes to complete each equation.

6. If △ + ○ = ☐ ,

then _____ − _____ = _____ .

7. If ▯ = ☐ + ☐ ,

then _____ = _____ − _____ .

8. 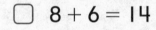 **Assessment Practice**

Which addition facts can help you find 8 − 2?
Choose two that apply. 🔵 1.OA.2.4

☐ 8 + 6 = 14

☐ 2 + 8 = 10

☐ 6 + 2 = 8

☐ 2 + 6 = 8

© Pearson Education, Inc. 1

Additional Practice 2-8
Solve Word Problems with Facts to 10

Another Look! You can use pictures to solve a number story.

Linda has 4 buttons.

She buys some more.

Now Linda has 7 buttons.

How many buttons did Linda buy?

$$\underline{4} \oplus \underline{3} = \underline{7}$$

$\underline{3}$ buttons

Draw a picture to solve.
Then write an equation to match.

1. Abby has 6 apples.
   Judy has 9 apples.

   How many more apples does Judy have than Abby?

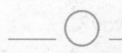

$$\underline{\hspace{1cm}} \bigcirc \underline{\hspace{1cm}} = \underline{\hspace{1cm}}$$

_____ more apples

2. Tim has 9 pears.

3 pears are yellow.

The rest are green.

How many pears are green?

_____ ◯ _____ = _____ green pears

3. Ian has 5 red balloons.

Max has 6 blue balloons.

How many balloons do

they have in all?

_____ ◯ _____ = _____ balloons

4. **Higher Order Thinking**

Use the chart. Write a number story.

Then write an equation to match your story.

Fruit	How Many?
Blueberries	
Raspberries	

_____

_____

_____

_____

_____ ◯ _____ = _____

5. ⓝ **Assessment Practice**

7 birds are on a branch.

Some birds fly away.

4 birds are left.

How many birds flew away?

 I.OA.I.I

Which subtraction equation matches the story?

Ⓐ 7 − 2 = 5 birds   Ⓒ 9 − 7 = 2 birds

Ⓑ 7 − 4 = 3 birds   Ⓓ 4 − 3 = I bird

Name _____

Another Look!

Karen has 5 purple and 4 yellow marbles.

She can only fit 5 marbles in her pocket.

What are all the ways she can put the marbles in her pocket?

Use a pattern to help you solve the problem.

Then complete the table to show all the ways.

The sum of the numbers in each row is __5__.

🟣	⚪
5	0
4	1
3	2
2	3
1	4

Use patterns to help you solve the problems.

1. Tom has 5 toy cars. He puts them in a box or on a shelf. Complete the table to show all the ways.

Box	Shelf
5	___
___	1
___	___
2	___
___	4
___	___

2. Kathy has 4 tulips and 4 roses. She wants to put 4 flowers in a vase. Complete the table to show all the ways.

🌷	🌹
0	___
___	___
___	2
3	___
___	0

Making a Fruit Bowl

Bill has 5 apples and 5 bananas.
He can put only 5 pieces of fruit in
a bowl.

He starts a table to show all the
ways he can put fruit in the bowl.

🍎	🍌
0	
1	
2	
3	
4	
5	

3. Generalize

What will be the same in each row of
the table? MP.8.1

_____

_____

4. Reasoning

Will the number of bananas be greater or
less as you move down the table?
How do you know? MP.2.1, MP.7.1

_____

_____

5. Look for Patterns

Write the missing numbers in the table.
How do you know your answers are
correct? 1.OA.2.3, 1.OA.3.6, MP.7.1

_____

_____

_____

_____

_____

Name _____

Another Look! There is more than one way to count on to add 2 + 8.

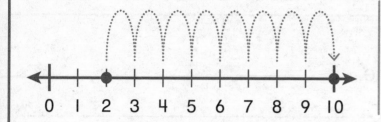

0 1 2 3 4 5 6 7 8 9 10

Start at 2, then take 8 jumps.

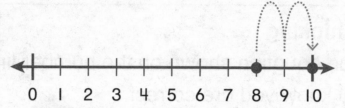

0 1 2 3 4 5 6 7 8 9 10

Start at 8, then take 2 jumps.

2 + 8 = __10__

If you start at 8 instead of 2, you don't have to count on as many. Remember, you get the same answer both ways.

HOME ACTIVITY Draw a number line and label it from 0–20. Give your child an addition fact, such as 5 + 9. Have your child use the number line to show counting on to add 5 and 9. Ask, "Can you show me more than one way to add these numbers (5 + 9 and 9 + 5)?" Repeat with other addition facts.

Use a number line to count on. Write each sum.

I. 9 + 4 = ___

2. 4 + 8 = ___

3. 9 + 7 = ___

Use a number line. Count on to find each sum.

4. $9 + 6 =$ ___   **5.** $7 + 4 =$ ___   **6.** $8 + 5 =$ ___

7. Higher Order Thinking

Write the addition equation shown on the number line.
Explain how you know you are correct.

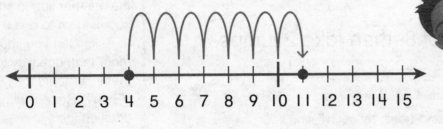

___ + ___ = ___

8. 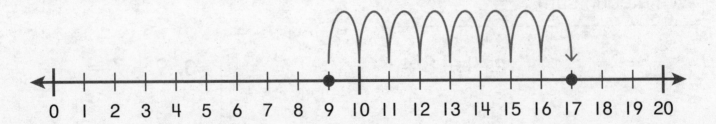 **Assessment Practice**

Which addition equation does the number line show? I.OA.3.5

0 1 2 3 4 5 6 7 8 9 10 11 12 13 14 15 16 17 18 19 20

Ⓐ $9 + 9 = 18$ Ⓑ $7 + 10 = 17$ Ⓒ $9 + 8 = 17$ Ⓓ $10 + 7 = 17$

Additional Practice 3-2
Count On to Add Using an Open Number Line

Another Look! You can count on to solve addition problems using an open number line.

8 + 9 = ?

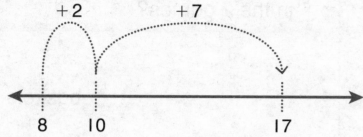

+2   +7

8   10   17

Start at ⟨8⟩ and count on ⟨9⟩ more.

8 + 9 = 17

HOME ACTIVITY Draw an open number line. Give your child an addition fact, such as 6 + 8. Ask, "Which number can you put at the beginning of the number line?" Have him or her show 2 different ways to add 8 to 6. Repeat with different addition facts.

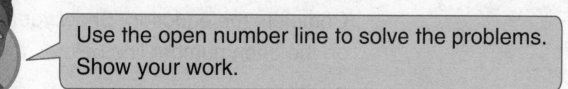

Use the open number line to solve the problems. Show your work.

1. 8 + 4 = ___

2. 8 + 7 = ___

3. Laura reads 8 pages on Monday.
She reads 6 pages on Tuesday.
How many pages did Laura read
in all?

_____ + _____ = _____

_____ pages

Write an equation to match.

4. Andy makes 6 baskets in a game.
He makes 7 baskets in the next game.
How many baskets did Andy make
in the 2 games?

_____ + _____ = _____

_____ baskets

5. Higher Order Thinking

Sam has 9 stamps.
He gets some more.
Now he has 18 stamps.
How many more stamps did Sam get?

6. Assessment Practice

Complete the equation. Show your work
on the open number line below.   1.OA.3.5

$5 + 7 =$ _____

Name _____

Another Look! Some facts are doubles facts. Some facts are not.

This is not a doubles fact.   This is a doubles fact.

The addends are not the same.

HOME ACTIVITY Divide a strip of paper into 6–10 parts so that it looks like a cube tower. Ask your child to count the parts. Then cut the strip in half vertically so you have 2 strips each with 6–10 parts. Ask your child how many are in each tower. Have him or her tell you the doubles fact that is represented. Repeat with other numbers (1–10).

In a doubles fact, both addends are the same.

$3 + 2 = \underline{5}$ $2 + 2 = \underline{4}$

Decide if each set of cubes shows a doubles fact.
Circle your answer. Write an equation to match the cubes.

1.

Doubles Fact   **NOT** Doubles Fact

____ + ____ = ____

2.

Doubles Fact   **NOT** Doubles Fact

____ + ____ = ____

Solve each fact. Circle the doubles. Use cubes to help you.

3.

_____ = 8 + 5

4.

5 + 5 = _____

5.

9 + 5 = _____

6.

10 + 10 = _____

7.

_____ = 7 + 6

8.

_____ = 9 + 9

9.

8 + 8 = _____

10.

_____ = 3 + 4

11.

7 + 7 = _____

12. Higher Order Thinking

Simone built the same number of toy cars and toy airplanes.

Show how Simone could have built 14 toys. Explain how you know.

13. **Assessment Practice**

Which could be a sum of a doubles fact?

Choose two that apply. 1.OA.3.6

☐ 19

☐ 18

☐ 17

☐ 16

Name _____

Additional Practice 3-4
Doubles Plus

Another Look! You can use doubles facts to solve doubles-plus facts.

$4 + 5 = ?$

5 is 1 more than 4.
So, $4 + 5$ is $4 + 4 + 1$.

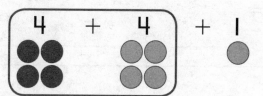

$4 + 4 = 8$
8 and 1 more is 9. So, $4 + 5 = 9$.

$2 + 4 = ?$
$2 + 4 = 2 + 2 + \underline{2}$

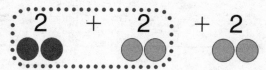

$\underline{2} + \underline{2} = \underline{4}$

So, $\underline{2} + \underline{4} = \underline{6}$.

HOME ACTIVITY Give your child a doubles fact, such as 3 + 3. Have your child use objects to show the doubles fact, such as two groups of 3 buttons. Ask, "How many in all?" Then add 1 more object to one of the groups. Ask, "What is the doubles-plus fact? How many in all now?" Repeat with other doubles facts.

Add the doubles. Then use the doubles facts to help you solve the doubles-plus facts.

1.
$\begin{array}{r} 3 \\ + 3 \\ \hline \square \end{array}$

$\begin{array}{r} 3 \\ + 5 \\ \hline \square \end{array}$

2.
$\begin{array}{r} 6 \\ + 6 \\ \hline \square \end{array}$

$\begin{array}{r} 6 \\ + 7 \\ \hline \square \end{array}$

Topic 3 | Lesson 4   Go Online | PearsonRealize.com   forty-three **43**

Draw 1 more cube. Use a doubles fact to help you add.

3.

Think: ____ + ____ = ____.

So, 7 + 8 = ____.

4.

Think: ____ + ____ = ____.

So, 9 + 10 = ____.

5. **Higher Order Thinking**

Write an equation for the problem.
Draw a picture to show your work.

Dan saw some cats and dogs.
He saw 1 more dog than cat.
How many dogs and cats did Dan see?

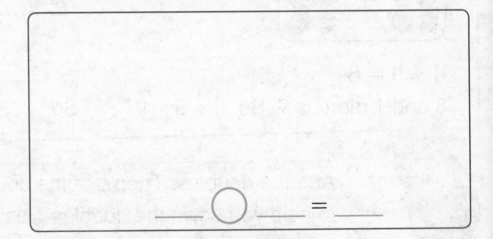

____ ◯ ____ = ____

6. **Assessment Practice**

Which doubles-plus fact should you use
to add 9 + 8? ⬤ 1.OA.3.6

Ⓐ 7 + 7 and 2 more

Ⓑ 8 + 8 and 1 more

Ⓒ 8 + 8 and 2 more

Ⓓ 9 + 9 and 1 more

7. **Assessment Practice**

Which doubles-plus fact should you use
to add 5 + 7? ⬤ 1.OA.3.6

Ⓐ 6 + 6 and 1 more

Ⓑ 5 + 5 and 1 more

Ⓒ 5 + 5 and 2 more

Ⓓ 4 + 4 and 2 more

Name _____

Another Look! You can make 10 to help you add.

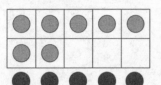
7 and 5 more.

$7 + 5 = ?$ Make 10.

10 and 2 more.

So, 7 + 5 and 10 + 2 have the same sum.

$10 + 2 = \underline{12}$ so, $7 + 5 = \underline{12}$.

HOME ACTIVITY Have your child use small objects to show 7 + 6. Tell your child to move some objects to make 10. Then have your child give the 2 equations: 10 + 3 = 13 so, 7 + 6 = 13.

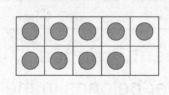
Draw counters to make 10. Then write the sums.

1.
$\begin{array}{r} 9 \\ + 6 \\ \hline ? \end{array}$

$\begin{array}{r} 10 \\ + 5 \\ \hline \square \end{array}$ so, $\begin{array}{r} 9 \\ + 6 \\ \hline \square \end{array}$

2.
$\begin{array}{r} 7 \\ + 6 \\ \hline ? \end{array}$

$\begin{array}{r} 10 \\ + 3 \\ \hline \square \end{array}$ so, $\begin{array}{r} 7 \\ + 6 \\ \hline \square \end{array}$

3.
$\begin{array}{r} 5 \\ + 6 \\ \hline ? \end{array}$

$\begin{array}{r} 10 \\ + 1 \\ \hline \square \end{array}$ so, $\begin{array}{r} 5 \\ + 6 \\ \hline \square \end{array}$

 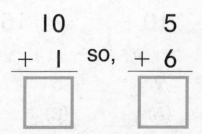

4.

$$\begin{array}{r} 9 \\ + 5 \\ \hline ? \end{array}$$

$$\begin{array}{r} 10 \\ + \ 4 \\ \hline \end{array} \quad \text{so,} \quad \begin{array}{r} 9 \\ + 5 \\ \hline \end{array}$$

5.

$$\begin{array}{r} 8 \\ + 3 \\ \hline ? \end{array}$$

$$\begin{array}{r} 10 \\ + \ 1 \\ \hline \end{array} \quad \text{so,} \quad \begin{array}{r} 8 \\ + 3 \\ \hline \end{array}$$

6.

$$\begin{array}{r} 4 \\ + 9 \\ \hline ? \end{array}$$

$$\begin{array}{r} 10 \\ + \ 3 \\ \hline \end{array} \quad \text{so,} \quad \begin{array}{r} 4 \\ + 9 \\ \hline \end{array}$$

7. Higher Order Thinking Circle any 2 numbers below.

5 6 7 8 9

Draw counters to make 10 using the numbers
you circled. Use 2 different colors.
Then write 2 addition equations to match the drawing.

10 + _____ = _____

So, _____ + _____ = _____.

8. **Assessment Practice**

Which number belongs in the ☐ ?

I.OA.3.6

10 + ☐ = 15   So, 9 + 6 = 15.

9   5   6   8
Ⓐ   Ⓑ   Ⓒ   Ⓓ

9. **Assessment Practice**

Which number belongs in the ☐ ?

I.OA.3.6

10 + 3 = 13   So, 8 + ☐ = 13.

5   6   7   8
Ⓐ   Ⓑ   Ⓒ   Ⓓ

Name _____

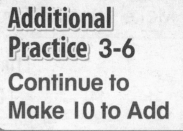
Another Look! You know how to add 10 to a number.
Making 10 to add can be a helpful addition strategy.

$3 + 9 = ?$

You can break apart either addend to help you make 10.

I broke apart the 3 into 1 and 2 to make 10.

	Think	Think	So
3	9	10	3
+ 9	+ 1	+ 2	+ 9
?	10	12	12

HOME ACTIVITY Start by reviewing with your child all the different ways to make 10 (e.g., 1 + 9, 2 + 8, etc.). Then give your child an addition fact with a sum from 11-19. Ask him or her to make 10 to add the two numbers. Repeat with different addition facts.

Make 10 to find each sum. Fill in the missing numbers.

		Think	Think	So
1.	9	9	10	9
	+ 8	+ ☐	+ ☐	+ 8
	?	10	☐	☐

		Think	Think	So
2.	2	9	10	2
	+ 9	+ ☐	+ ☐	+ 9
	?	10	☐	☐

Make 10 to find each sum. Fill in the missing numbers.

		Think		So
3.	7	10		7
	+ 5	+ ☐		+ 5
	?	☐		☐

		Think		So
4.	4	10		4
	+ 9	+ ☐		+ 9
	?	☐		☐

		Think		So
5.	8	10		8
	+ 9	+ ☐		+ 9
	?	☐		☐

		Think		So
6.	7	10		7
	+ 8	+ ☐		+ 8
	?	☐		☐

		Think		So
7.	9	10		9
	+ 9	+ ☐		+ 9
	?	☐		☐

		Think		So
8.	5	10		5
	+ 6	+ ☐		+ 6
	?	☐		☐

9. **Higher Order Thinking**
Jazmin says she can make 10
to solve 6 + 3. Is she correct?
Explain how you know.

_____

_____

_____

10. 🌀 **Assessment Practice**
Which shows how to make 10
to add 8 + 8? 🌀 I.OA.3.6

Ⓐ 8 + 8 + 2

Ⓑ 8 + 2 + 6

Ⓒ 8 + 1 + 8

Ⓓ 8 + 5 + 4

Name _____

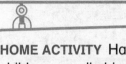

Another Look! You can use different strategies to solve problems.

5 and 6 are 1 apart. They are near doubles.

$$\begin{array}{r} 5 \\ +6 \\ \hline ? \end{array}$$

$$\begin{array}{r} 5 \\ +5 \\ \hline \boxed{10} \end{array}$$

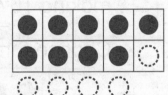

$$\begin{array}{r} 5 \\ +6 \\ \hline \boxed{11} \end{array}$$

9 is close to 10. Make 10.

$$\begin{array}{r} 9 \\ +5 \\ \hline ? \end{array}$$

$$\begin{array}{r} 10 \\ +4 \\ \hline \boxed{14} \end{array} \quad so \quad \begin{array}{r} 9 \\ +5 \\ \hline \boxed{14} \end{array}$$

Find each sum. Choose a strategy to use.

1. $\begin{array}{r} 5 \\ +7 \\ \hline \end{array}$ Think: 5 and 7 are 2 apart.

2. $\begin{array}{r} 8 \\ +3 \\ \hline \end{array}$ Think: 8 is close to 10.

3.
$$
\begin{array}{r}
9 \\
+\ 3 \\
\hline
\end{array}
$$

4.
$$
\begin{array}{r}
7 \\
+\ 7 \\
\hline
\end{array}
$$

5.
$$
\begin{array}{r}
7 \\
+\ 9 \\
\hline
\end{array}
$$

6. **Higher Order Thinking**

Write a story problem that can be solved by making 10.

Then explain how to solve the problem.

7. **Assessment Practice**

Which equations are **NOT** correct ways to solve the problem below by making 10?

Choose three that apply.   I.OA.3.6

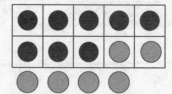

☐ $6 + 4 = 10; \ 10 + 0 = 10$

☐ $7 + 3 = 10; \ 10 + 1 = 11$

☐ $8 + 2 = 10; \ 10 + 4 = 14$

☐ $9 + 1 = 10; \ 10 + 3 = 13$

Name _____

Another Look! You can use counters and equations to solve problems.

Jake hits 8 baseballs.

He hits 5 fewer baseballs than Andy.

How many baseballs did Andy hit?

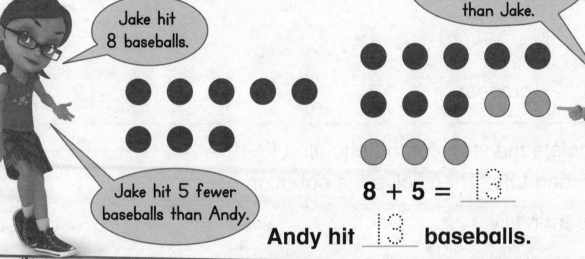

Jake hit 8 baseballs.

Jake hit 5 fewer baseballs than Andy.

That means Andy hit 5 more baseballs than Jake.

$8 + 5 = \underline{13}$

Andy hit $\underline{13}$ **baseballs.**

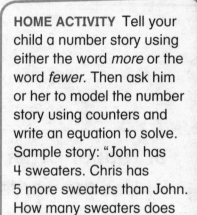

 Draw counters and write equations to solve.

1. Maggie sees 3 more foxes than Henry.

   Henry sees 4 foxes.

   How many foxes did Maggie see?

   ____ ◯ ____ = ____ ____ foxes

2. Desiree has 2 fewer cards than Wendy.

   Desiree has 9 cards.

   How many cards did Wendy have?

   ____ ◯ ____ = ____ ____ cards

3. 3 green grapes and 10 red grapes
are in a bowl.
How many grapes are in the bowl?

____ ◯ ____ = ____   ____ grapes

4. 8 cats play. Some more cats come
to play. 15 cats are playing now.
How many cats came to play with the
8 cats?

____ ◯ ____ = ____   ____ cats

---

5. Higher Order Thinking Complete the story for the equation $9 + 4 = ?$
Use the words **James**, **fewer**, and **Lily**. Then solve the equation.

James sees 4 _____ birds than Lily.

_____ sees 9 birds.

How many birds did _____ see?    ____ ◯ ____ = ____

---

6. **Assessment Practice**
Chad made 6 fewer sandwiches than Sarah.
Chad made 7 sandwiches.
How many sandwiches did Sarah make?

🌐 I.OA.I.I

Ⓐ $7 - 6 = 1$ sandwich

Ⓑ $7 - 1 = 6$ sandwiches

Ⓒ $7 + 6 = 13$ sandwiches

Ⓓ $6 + 10 = 16$ sandwiches

Practice · Video · Tools · Games

Additional Practice 3-9
Critique Reasoning

Another Look! Lidia has 10 pennies. Jon has 8 pennies.

Sheila says Jon has 2 fewer pennies than Lidia because $10 - 8 = 2$.

Do you agree or not agree with Sheila?

Lidia ○○○○○○○○○○

Jon ○○○○○○○○

$10 - 8 = 2$

I used a picture and equation to show that Jon has 2 fewer pennies than Lidia. I agree with Sheila.

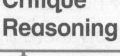

 Circle your answer. Use pictures, words, or equations to explain.

1. Anna says that $7 + 4$ is equal to $3 + 9$ because both equal 11. Do you **agree** or **not agree** with Anna?

Agree   **Not Agree**

The Birds

9 birds are on a fence. Some more come.

Now there are 18 birds on the fence.

How many more birds came to the fence?

Help Max solve the problem.

Answer the items below to check his thinking.

2. Explain

Max says that he can use a doubles fact to solve this problem.

Do you agree? Explain. MP.3.1

3. Model

How can Max use words or drawings to show the problem? MP.4.1

_____

_____

_____

_____

_____

_____

_____

_____

© Pearson Education, Inc. 1

Name _____

Another Look! You can count back on a number line to subtract.

$12 - 5 = ?$

Start at the number you are subtracting from.
Count back the number that you are subtracting.

> I started at 12.
> Then I counted back 5.
> I ended at 7.

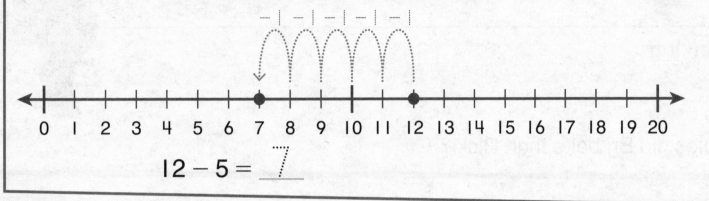

$12 - 5 = \underline{7}$

HOME ACTIVITY Draw a number line and label it 0-20. Give your child a subtraction fact, such as $11 - 4$. Ask, "How can you use counting back or counting on to subtract?" Have your child use the number line to subtract 4 from 11. Repeat with other subtraction facts.

Find the difference. Use the number line to count back or count on.

1. $13 - 8 = \underline{}$

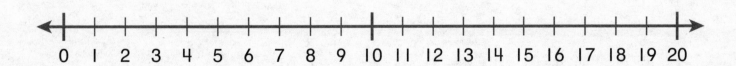

Solve the problems.

2. Make Sense Help Patty find $11 - 4$ on a number line. Fill in the blanks.

Start at _____ . Count back _____ . $11 - 4 =$ _____

How can you check that your solution makes sense?

3. Higher Order Thinking

Bri bakes 14 pies.

Ricki bakes 9 pies.

How many more pies did Bri bake than Ricki?

Write an equation.

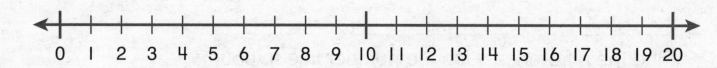

_____ ◯ _____ = _____   _____ more pies

4. 🦩 **Assessment Practice**

Use the number line to find $13 - 8$.

Show your work. 🦩 1.OA.3.5

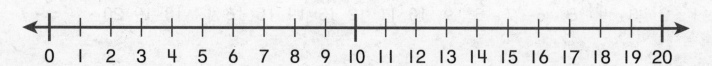

$13 - 8 =$ _____

© Pearson Education, Inc. 1

Name _____

Practice Video Tools Games

Additional Practice 4-2
Make 10 to Subtract

Another Look!

Breaking numbers apart to make 10 can help you subtract.

$13 - 4 = ?$

First, take away 3 to make 10.

Then, take away 1 more because you need to subtract 4 in all.

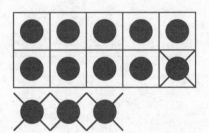

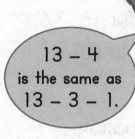 

13 – 4 is the same as 13 – 3 – 1.

$13 - 3 = \underline{10}$ $10 - 1 = \underline{9}$ $13 - 4 = \underline{9}$

HOME ACTIVITY Write $12 - 7 = ?$ on a piece of paper. Have your child use small objects to find the difference. Tell your child to make a 10 to subtract: by adding on to get 10 or by subtracting to get 10. Have your child explain each step of the process as he or she solves the problem.

 Make 10 to subtract. Complete each subtraction fact.

1.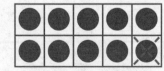
$14 - 5 = \underline{9}$

2.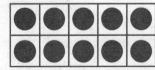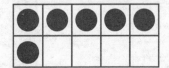
$16 - 7 = \underline{}$

3.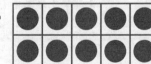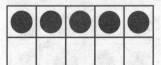
$15 - 8 = \underline{}$

Show your work. Draw counters in the ten-frames.

4. Number Sense

Show how you can make 10 to find $16 - 8$.

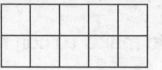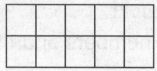

$16 - 8 = \underline{\quad}$

5. Higher Order Thinking

Write a story problem for $15 - 6$.
Show how to make 10 to solve
the problem.

Then complete the equation.

$15 - 6 = \underline{\quad}$

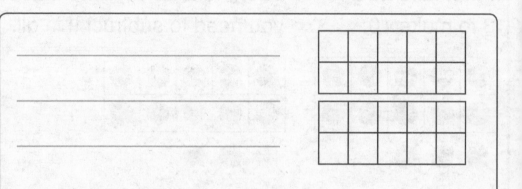

6. 🔾 Assessment Practice Draw lines.

Match each pair of ten-frames with the equations
that show how to solve by making 10. 🔾 1.OA.3.6

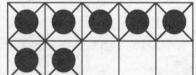 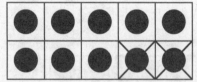 $17 - 7 = 10, 10 - 2 = 8$

$17 - 8 = 9, 9 - 1 = 8$

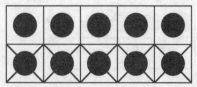  $12 - 2 = 10, 10 - 5 = 5$

$12 - 2 = 10, 10 - 4 = 6$

Another Look!

Counting on to make 10 can help you subtract.

$16 - 7 = ?$

> You added 3 and then 6 more.
> $3 + 6 = 9$. You added 9 in all.
> So, $16 - 7 = \underline{9}$.

Start with 7.

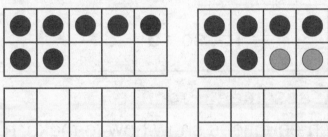

Add 3 to make 10.

Then add 6 more to make 16.

> Subtract. Count on to make 10.
> Show your work, and complete the facts.

1. $17 - 8 = ?$

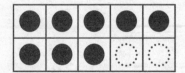

> Remember! Start by counting on to make a 10.

$8 + \underline{2} = 10$ $10 + \underline{7} = 17$

$8 + \underline{} = 17$, so $17 - 8 = \underline{}$.

Subtract. Count on to make 10.
Show your work, and complete the facts.

2. $13 - 8 = ?$

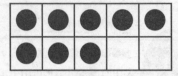

$8 + \underline{\quad} = 10$

$10 + \underline{\quad} = 13$

$8 + \underline{\quad} = 13$, so $13 - 8 = \underline{\quad}$.

3. $15 - 8 = ?$

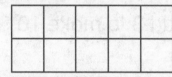

$8 + \underline{\quad} = 10$

$10 + \underline{\quad} = 15$

$8 + \underline{\quad} = 15$, so $15 - 8 = \underline{\quad}$.

4. Higher Order Thinking

Andrew scores 11 goals in 2 games.
He scored 8 goals in the first game.
How many goals did Andrew score in
the second game?

Make 10 to solve. Show your work.

$\underline{\quad} \bigcirc \underline{\quad} = \underline{\quad}$

Andrew scored $\underline{\quad}$ goals.

5. Assessment Practice

Which equations show how to make 10 to
solve $11 - 5 = ?$ I.OA.3.6

Ⓐ $5 + 5 = 10, 10 + 2 = 12, 5 + 2 = 7$

Ⓑ $11 + 5 = 16$

Ⓒ $5 + 5 = 10, 10 + 1 = 11, 5 + 1 = 6$

Ⓓ $10 + 5 = 15$

Practice Video Tools Games

Another Look! You can make a fact family for each model.

17

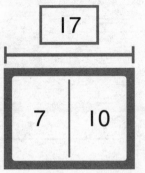

| 7 | 10 |

$7 + 10 = 17$
$10 + 7 = 17$
$17 - 10 = 7$
$17 - 7 = 10$

15

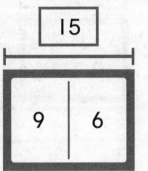

| 9 | 6 |

$9 + 6 = 15$
$6 + 9 = 15$
$15 - 6 = 9$
$15 - 9 = 6$

Fact families use the same numbers.

HOME ACTIVITY Write an addition problem, such as $9 + 4 = ?$ Have your child find the sum and write the related addition fact. $(4 + 9 = 13)$ Then ask your child to write the 2 related subtraction equations to complete the fact family. $(13 - 9 = 4$ and $13 - 4 = 9)$ Continue with several other fact families.

Write the fact family for each model.

1.

18

| 10 | 8 |

$10 + 8 = 18$
$\_\_ + \_\_ = \_\_$
$18 - 10 = 8$
$\_\_ - \_\_ = \_\_$

2.

14

| 9 | 5 |

$\_\_ + \_\_ = \_\_$
$\_\_ + \_\_ = \_\_$
$\_\_ - \_\_ = \_\_$
$\_\_ - \_\_ = \_\_$

Write the fact family for each model.

3.

| 12 |
| 3 | 9 |

___ + ___ = ___

___ + ___ = ___

___ − ___ = ___

___ − ___ = ___

4.

| 14 |
| 8 | 6 |

___ + ___ = ___

___ + ___ = ___

___ − ___ = ___

___ − ___ = ___

5. Higher Order Thinking Circle the
3 numbers that make up a fact family.
Write the fact family.

5   7   8   4   13

___ + ___ = ___

___ + ___ = ___

___ − ___ = ___

___ − ___ = ___

6.  **Assessment Practice**

Write a fact family to match the picture. 🔊 1.OA.2.4

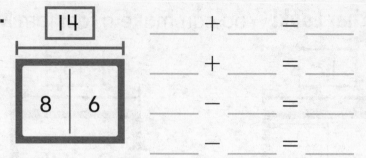

How does the solution to one problem help you solve another problem?

___ + ___ = ___   ___ − ___ = ___

___ + ___ = ___   ___ − ___ = ___

Name _____

Another Look!

An addition fact can help you solve a related subtraction fact.

$18 - 8 = ?$

18

8 | 10

$8 + 10 = 18$
$18 - 8 = 10$

$15 - 6 = ?$

15

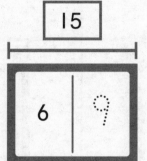

6 | 9

$6 + \underline{9} = 15$
$15 - 6 = \underline{9}$

HOME ACTIVITY Write a subtraction problem for your child to solve. Have him or her say a related addition fact to help solve the subtraction problem. Provide pennies or other small objects to be used as counters, if necessary. Repeat using different subtraction problems.

Complete each model.
Then complete the equations.

1. $11 - 6 = ?$

11

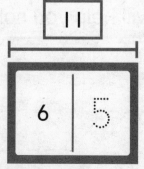

6 | 5

$6 + \underline{5} = 11$
$11 - 6 = \underline{5}$

2. $12 - 9 = ?$

12

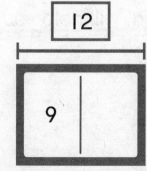

9 |

$9 + \underline{} = 12$
$12 - 9 = \underline{}$

Complete each model.
Then complete the equations.

3. What addition fact can Amy use to find
10 − 6?

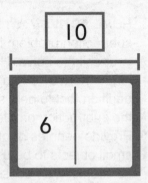

10

6

6 + ____ = 10

10 − 6 = ____

4. What addition fact can Dan use to find
16 − 8?

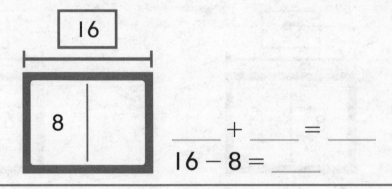

16

8

____ + ____ = ____

16 − 8 = ____

5. Higher Order Thinking

Draw the missing shape. Then explain how you know your answer is correct.

If ⬯ + ◯ = △ ,

then △ − ⬯ = ____ .

_____

_____

_____

6. 🔵 **Assessment Practice**

Write an addition fact that will help you
solve 14 − 9 = ?. 🔵 1.OA.2.4

____ + ____ = ____

7. 🔵 **Assessment Practice**

Write an addition fact will help you solve
18 − 10 = ?. 🔵 1.OA.2.4

____ + ____ = ____

© Pearson Education, Inc. 1

Name _____

Another Look!

You can use a related addition fact to help you subtract.

$8 - 5 = ?$

Think: $5 + ? = 8$

You can use the cubes to add.

If $5 + 3 = 8$, then $8 - 5 = 3$.

$9 - 7 = ?$

If $\underline{7} + \underline{2} = \underline{9}$,

then $\underline{9} - \underline{7} = \underline{2}$.

HOME ACTIVITY Collect 15 pennies to use as counters. Make a subtraction problem for your child to solve by removing some of the pennies. Have him or her tell you the subtraction equation. Then have your child say the related addition equation that helped him or her subtract.

Complete the addition fact.
Then solve the related subtraction fact.

1. $16 - 7 = ?$

If $7 + \underline{9} = 16$,

then $16 - 7 = \underline{9}$.

2. $14 - 6 = ?$

If $6 + \underline{} = 14$,

then $14 - 6 = \underline{}$.

3. $17 - 8 = ?$

If $8 + \underline{} = 17$,

then $17 - 8 = \underline{}$.

4. $13 - 7 = ?$

If $7 + \underline{} = 13$,

then $13 - 7 = \underline{}$.

5. Reasoning

Josh has 12 pencils.

He gives some of them to his friends.

Now he has 7 pencils left.

How many pencils did Josh give to his friends?

How does the word problem help me understand what the numbers mean?

_____ + _____ = _____

_____ − _____ = _____   _____ pencils

6. Higher Order Thinking

Your friend says he can use the addition

fact $4 + 7 = 11$ to help find $11 - 3$.

Is your friend correct?

Explain your answer.

7. Assessment Practice

Which related addition fact helps you

solve $12 - 3 = ?$ 1.OA.2.4

 Ⓐ $10 + 3 = 13$

 Ⓑ $3 + 6 = 9$

 Ⓒ $2 + 10 = 12$

 Ⓓ $3 + 9 = 12$

8. Assessment Practice

Which related addition fact helps you

solve $17 - 7 = ?$ 1.OA.2.4

 Ⓐ $6 + 7 = 13$

 Ⓑ $7 + 8 = 15$

 Ⓒ $10 + 7 = 17$

 Ⓓ $10 + 4 = 14$

Name _____

Another Look! You can use different strategies to solve problems.

Use an addition fact to solve a related subtraction problem.

$$18 - 9 = ?$$

18

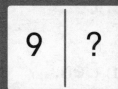
9 | ?

$$9 + 9 = 18$$
$$18 - 9 = 9$$

Count on to make 10.

$$14 - 6 = ?$$

Choose the strategy that works best.

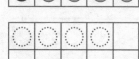

$$6 + \underline{4} = 10$$
$$10 + \underline{4} = 14$$
$$14 - 6 = \underline{8}$$

HOME ACTIVITY Write a subtraction equation like $19 - 9 = ?$ Ask your child to solve the problem. Ask what strategy he or she used to solve the problem, for example, making 10, using a related addition fact, counting, or another strategy.

Find each difference.

1. 11   Think: 11 is close to 10.
  $-\ 5$
  ___
  | 6 |

2. 15   Think: Can an addition
  $-\ 9$ fact I know help me?
  ___
  | |

Find each difference.

3. 15
      − 7
      ☐

4. 14
      − 5
      ☐

5. 12
      − 9
      ☐

---

6. Higher Order Thinking

Use pictures, numbers, or words to solve the problem.

Beth finds 13 dolls in her room.
4 of the dolls have curly hair.
How many dolls do **NOT** have curly hair?

_____ − _____ = _____ dolls

7. **Assessment Practice**

Ben has 10 baseballs.
Andy has 2 fewer than Ben.
How many baseballs does Andy have?

Which addition facts could help you solve the problem?
Choose two that apply. I.OA.2.4

☐ 10 + 0 = 10

☐ 8 + 2 = 10

☐ 9 + 1 = 10

☐ 2 + 8 = 10

Name _____

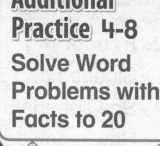

Another Look! You can solve word problems even when you do not know the starting number.

Carrie works on Monday and Tuesday.
She works 10 hours on Tuesday.
She works 20 hours in all.
How many hours did Carrie work on Monday?

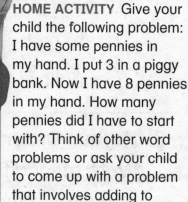

Write an equation to show the problem.

$$\underline{10} \ \oplus \ 10 \ = \ 20$$

Hours on Monday   Hours on Tuesday   Hours in All

Carrie worked __10__ hours on Monday.

HOME ACTIVITY Give your child the following problem: I have some pennies in my hand. I put 3 in a piggy bank. Now I have 8 pennies in my hand. How many pennies did I have to start with? Think of other word problems or ask your child to come up with a problem that involves adding to or subtracting from an unknown amount.

Write an equation to match the story and solve.
Draw a picture to help.

1. Jim picks some red flowers.
   He also picks 7 yellow flowers.
   He picks 15 flowers in all.
   How many red flowers did Jim pick?

   $$\underline{} \ \oplus \ \underline{7} \ = \ \underline{15}$$

   ____ red flowers

2. Reasoning

Sloane has 13 dollars.

She spends 5 dollars at the store.

How many dollars did Sloane have left?

Draw a picture and write an equation to solve.

_____ ◯ _____ = _____

_____ dollars

3. Higher Order Thinking

Write an addition and a subtraction

equation to match the problem. Then solve.

Li has 14 crackers.

Joe has 8 crackers.

How many more crackers does Li have

than Joe?

_____ ◯ _____ = _____

_____ ◯ _____ = _____

Li has _____ more crackers than Joe.

4. 🔵 Assessment Practice

Charlie makes some muffins for a bake sale.

Then his mother gives him 8 more muffins.

Now he has 20 muffins.

How many muffins did Charlie make? 1.OA.1.1

Ⓐ 19 muffins

Ⓑ 16 muffins

Ⓒ 13 muffins

Ⓓ 12 muffins

Name _____

Additional Practice 4-9
Reasoning

Another Look! You can write a number story for each problem.
Then you can complete the equation to match.

$12 - 5 = \underline{7}$

Cindy picks 12 lemons.
She gives 5 away.
How many lemons does Cindy have now?

Now Cindy has 7 lemons.

$9 + 5 = \underline{14}$

Sarah picks $\underline{9}$ flowers.
Then she picks $\underline{5}$ more.
How many flowers does Sarah pick in all?

Sarah picks $\underline{14}$ flowers in all.

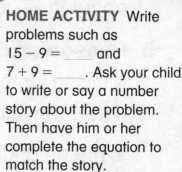
HOME ACTIVITY Write problems such as $15 - 9 = \underline{}$ and $7 + 9 = \underline{}$. Ask your child to write or say a number story about the problem. Then have him or her complete the equation to match the story.

Write a number story to show the problem.
Complete the equation to match your story.

1. $14 - 8 = \underline{}$

_____

_____

_____

_____

2. $8 + 8 = \underline{}$

_____

_____

_____

_____

Socks Melissa finds 5 blue socks.

Then she finds 3 purple socks.

She writes addition and subtraction stories
about the socks.

3. **Reasoning**

Melissa writes this question about the socks:

How many socks did I find in all?

Write an addition equation to solve Melissa's question.   I.OA.I.I, MP.2.I

_____ ◯ _____ = _____   _____ socks

4. **Reasoning**

Melissa writes another question about the socks:

How many more blue socks than purple socks did I find?

Write a subtraction equation to solve Melissa's question.   I.OA.I.I, MP.2.I

_____ ◯ _____ = _____   _____ more blue socks

5. **Explain**

Are the addition and subtraction equations
you wrote for Melissa in the same fact
family? Circle **Yes** or **No.** Use words,
pictures, or equations to explain.

I.OA.2.4, MP.3.I

Yes   **No**

Practice Video Tools Games

Another Look! You can find the missing number in an addition or subtraction equation. Add counters to the empty side of the mat until there are 17 in all.

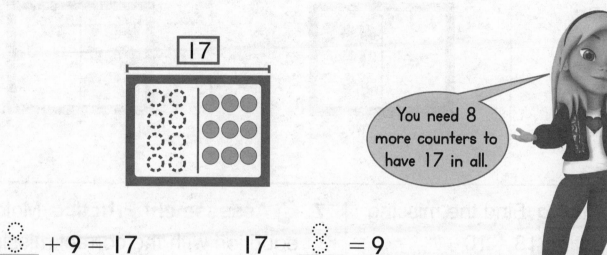

17

You need 8 more counters to have 17 in all.

$\underset{..}{8} + 9 = 17$ $17 - \underset{..}{8} = 9$

HOME ACTIVITY On a piece of paper, write an equation with a missing number, such as $7 + \underline{\quad} = 16$. Give your child a pile of small objects and ask her or him to find the correct amount of objects for the missing number. Repeat with another equation with a different operation, such as $18 - \underline{\quad} = 8$.

Draw the missing counters. Then complete the equation.

1.

14

$8 + \underline{\quad} = 14$

2.

20

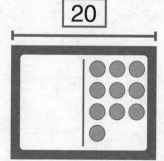

$20 - 10 = \underline{\quad}$

3. _____ $= 8 + 5$

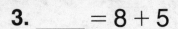

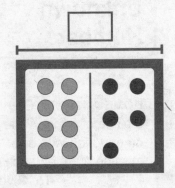

4. $16 -$ _____ $= 9$

16

5. $9 +$ _____ $= 18$

18

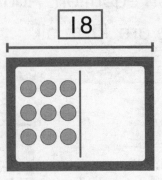

6. Higher Order Thinking Find the missing number in the equation $18 = 10 +$ _____. Then write a story that matches the problem.

7. 🌀 **Assessment Practice** Match each equation with the correct missing number. 🌀 1.OA.4.8

$17 -$ _____ $= 10$ 8

_____ $+ 6 = 14$ 5

$4 +$ _____ $= 9$ 7

_____ $- 10 = 10$ 20

Name _____

Another Look! Use connecting cubes to model true or false equations of different types.

Draw lines to match the cubes.

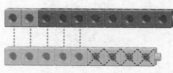

If both sides are not equal, then the equation is false.

$4 = 4$

This equation is **true**.

$5 = 2 + 7$

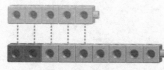

This equation is **false**.

$2 + 8 = 9 - 4$

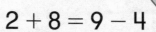

This equation is **false**.

HOME ACTIVITY Write a plus sign, minus sign, and equal sign, each on a separate notecard or scrap of paper. Gather 20 small objects, such as buttons or pennies. Set up the notecards and objects to show true or false equations, such as $3 + 5 = 9 - 1$ or $6 - 2 = 3 + 3$. Ask your child to tell if each equation is **true** or **false**.

Draw lines to match the cubes. Tell if each equation is **True** or **False**.

1. $9 = 7 + 2$

True   False

2. $7 + 3 = 9 - 3$

True   False

3. $10 - 2 = 1 + 7$

True   False

4. $10 - 2 = 7 + 4$

True   False

5. $6 = 9 - 5$

True   False

6. $8 + 5 = 10 + 3$

True   False

7. Higher Order Thinking Jamie says that $19 - 10$ is equal to $20 - 10$ because both use subtraction. Is Jamie correct? Explain why or why not.

_____

_____

_____

_____

8. ⬤ **Assessment Practice** Which equations below are **true**? Choose two that apply.

⬤ I.OA.4.7

☐ $8 - 7 = 11 - 10$

☐ $12 - 4 = 6 + 3$

☐ $10 - 1 = 9 + 2$

☐ $9 + 2 = 10 + 1$

Name _____

Practice   Video   Tools   Games

Another Look! Solving one side of a true equation can help you determine the value of the other side.

$$9 + \underline{\quad} = 7 + 8$$

Both sides of a true equation must have the same value.

First, solve $7 + 8$.

$$7 + 8 = 15$$

Next, solve $9 + \underline{?} = 15$.

$$9 + \underline{6} = 15$$

So, $9 + \underline{6} = 7 + 8$.

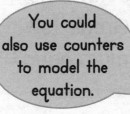
You could also use counters to model the equation.

HOME ACTIVITY Write a number between 0 and 20. Ask your child to write an addition or subtraction fact that would equal the number. Repeat with other numbers. Have your child give you a number and then you give an addition or subtraction fact. Ask if you made a true or false equation.

Write the missing numbers to make the equations true. Draw counters to help.

1.

$$7 + \underline{\quad} = 8 + 6$$
$$8 + 6 = \underline{\quad}$$
$$7 + \underline{\quad} = \underline{\quad}$$

2.

$$2 + 4 = 16 - \underline{\quad}$$
$$2 + 4 = \underline{\quad}$$
$$\underline{\quad} = 16 - \underline{\quad}$$

3. **Reasoning** Greg has 15 hats. Tamara has 10 hats. She wants to have the same number of hats as Greg. How many more hats does Tamara need?

$15 = 10 +$ ____

____ more

4. **Reasoning** Laila uses the same number of counters as Frank. What number would make this equation true?

$8 + 1 = 16 -$ ____

5. **Higher Order Thinking** Write the missing number that makes the equation true. Use pictures or words to explain how you know.

$3 + 4 = 8 -$ ____

6. 🔵 **Assessment Practice** Draw an arrow to show which number will make the equation true. 🔵 I.OA.4.7

$$1 \quad 2 \quad 3 \quad 4 \quad 5 \quad 6 \quad 7 \quad 8$$

$$4 + \underline{\quad} = 1 + 8$$

Name _____

Another Look! When you add three numbers, look for facts you know. Then add the third number.

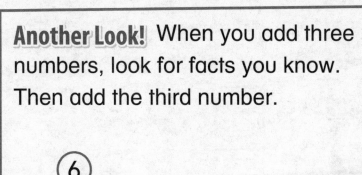

6 + 4 = 10
10 + 3 = 13

+3

13

I can add the numbers in a different order.

The sum is the same.

6 + 3 = 9
9 + 4 = 13

+

13

HOME ACTIVITY Tell your child three numbers that have a sum less than or equal to 20. Have him or her add the three numbers to find the sum. Ask your child to think aloud as he or she adds the first two numbers, and then the third number to that sum. Repeat with several sets of numbers.

 Find each sum using different ways. Add the circled numbers first. Then add the third number.

1.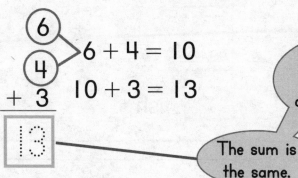

5 + 5 = ___
___ + 2 = ___

+

2 + 5 = ___
___ + 5 = ___

+

Add the numbers shown. Circle the numbers you add first.

2.  6
6
3 + ☐

☐ turtles

3.  4
5
6 + ☐

☐ fish

4. **Higher Order Thinking** Explain how to add $3 + 3 + 4$. Use pictures, numbers, or words.

5. 🦉 **Assessment Practice** Matt buys 3 blocks of wood, 6 tires, and 3 cans of paint. Matt wants to know how many items he bought in all.

Which two numbers can he add first to use a doubles fact? 🦉 I.OA.2.3

Ⓐ $3 + 6$

Ⓑ $6 + 3$

Ⓒ $3 + 3$

Ⓓ $6 + 6$

Name _____

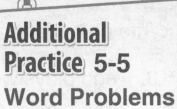
Another Look! You can group addends in different ways.
Then you can write an equation.

 +  +

Sally has some fruit.
She has 3 apples,
5 bananas, and 5 pears.
How many pieces of fruit
does she have in all?

First, add the bananas and pears.

$5 + 5 = \underline{10}$

Then add the apples.

$\underline{10} + \underline{3} = \underline{13}$

Sally has $\underline{13}$ pieces of fruit in all.

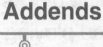
HOME ACTIVITY Gather several different kinds of small objects, such as buttons, paper clips, and pennies. Tell your child a word problem using the objects. Have your child add the objects together, telling you how many in all.

Find each sum. Choose a way to group the addends.

1.

___ + ___ + ___ = ___

2.

___ + ___ + ___ = ___

Write an equation to solve each problem.

3. Todd plays with some blocks. He has 3 red blocks, 3 yellow blocks, and 6 blue blocks. How many blocks is Todd playing with in all?

_____ + _____ + _____ = _____

_____ blocks

4. Emma has 7 green beads, some purple beads, and 6 yellow beads. She has 17 beads in all. How many purple beads does Emma have?

_____ + _____ + _____ = _____

_____ purple beads

5. Rita plants 3 rows of carrots, 4 rows of onions, and 7 rows of lettuce. How many rows of vegetables does Rita plant in all?

_____ + _____ + _____ = _____

_____ rows

6. Julien builds 8 tables, 3 chairs, and 4 desks. How many pieces of furniture does Julien build in all?

_____ + _____ + _____ = _____

_____ pieces

7. **Higher Order Thinking** Write a story problem about the lunchroom that matches the equation $5 + 8 + 2 = 15$.

_____

_____

_____

_____

8. 🐢 **Assessment Practice** At the animal shelter, Kim feeds 2 rabbits, 6 dogs, and 4 cats. How many animals does Kim feed in all? 🐢 1.OA.1.2

| 18 | 16 | 15 | 12 |
| Ⓐ | Ⓑ | Ⓒ | Ⓓ |

© Pearson Education, Inc. 1

Name _____

Practice Video Tools Games

Additional
Practice 5-6
Solve Addition
and Subtraction
Word Problems

Another Look! You can use addition or subtraction to solve word problems.

Bill has 10 more berries than Ken.

Bill has 14 berries.

How many berries does Ken have?

Bill has 10 more than Ken. I will subtract.

I will start with 10 red counters. Then I will add yellow counters to make 14. How many yellow counters are there?

HOME ACTIVITY Model a comparison situation, such as, Tom has 3 more cards than Julie. Tom has 10 cards. How many cards does Julie have? Have your child use small objects to model the story. Then ask him or her to write an equation that matches the story. Repeat with other similar comparison problems.

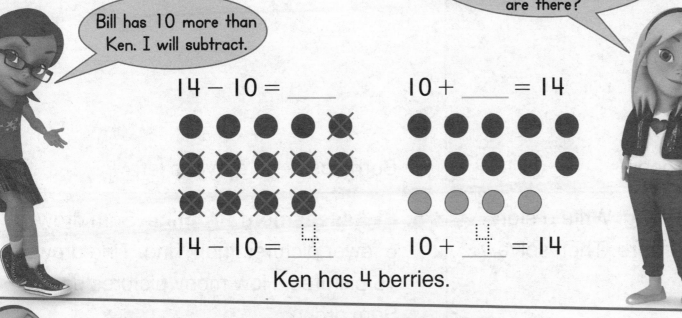

14 − 10 = _____

10 + _____ = 14

14 − 10 = 4

10 + 4 = 14

Ken has 4 berries.

Draw counters to show the problem. Then solve.

1. Shelly has 10 pumpkins. She gives some to Nola. Now Shelly has 6 pumpkins. How many pumpkins did Shelly give Nola?

_____ ◯ _____ = _____

Shelly gave Nola _____ pumpkins.

2. Victor writes 10 more poems than Ann.
Ann writes 10 poems.
How many poems does Victor write?

____ ◯ ____ = ____

Victor writes ____ poems.

3. Barb has 13 crayons. She gives 6 crayons to Javier. How many crayons does Barb have left?

____ ◯ ____ = ____

Barb has ____ crayons left.

4. Higher Order Thinking Write a story that uses the word **more**. Then solve.

_____

_____

_____

____ ◯ ____ = ____

_____

5. 🎯 **Assessment Practice** Sam draws 6 fewer pictures than Tina. Tina draws 15 pictures. How many pictures does Sam draw?

Draw or cross out counters and write an equation to match the story. 🔵 I.OA.I.I

● ● ● ● ●
● ● ● ● ●
● ● ● ●

____ ◯ ____ = ____

Sam draws ____ pictures.

Name _____

 Additional Practice 5-7
Precision

Another Look! You can write a missing number to make an equation true.

$$3 + 9 = \underline{} + 6$$

First, solve the side you know.

$$3 + 9 = \underline{12}$$

> I know the meaning of the = symbol is "the same as".

Then, use what you know to solve the other side.

$$12 = \underline{6} + 6$$

> 12 is a double: 6 + 6. The missing number is 6!

$$3 + 9 = 6 + 6 \text{ is the same as } 12 = 12.$$

HOME ACTIVITY Place 2 small groups of objects (less than or equal to 10) on the table. Ask your child to tell you the addition problem that is represented (for example, 5 + 7 = 12). Then have him or her rearrange the objects into a different 2 groups. Ask your child again to tell you the addition fact that is represented (for example, 9 + 3 = 12). Help your child write an equation that shows that his or her addition fact is equal to yours (for example, 5 + 7 = 9 + 3).

> Write the missing number to make the equation true. Then, write the number that makes both sides equal.

1. $\boxed{} - 0 = 7 + 8$

___ = ___

2. $6 + 4 = \boxed{} + 9$

___ = ___

3. $8 - 5 = 13 - \boxed{}$

___ = ___

Checkers James and Amy played 12 games of checkers last week. This week they played 7 games on Monday and 2 games on Wednesday.

4. **Explain** James and Amy play 3 more games. They have played the same number of games as last week. Fill in the blanks to make the equation true. Use $+$, $-$, or $=$. 🐢 1.OA.4.7, MP.3.1

12 ◯ 7 ◯ 2 ◯ 3 _____

Explain how you chose the symbols.

_____

_____

_____

_____

How do you know the equation is true?

_____

_____

5. **Be Precise** Amy lost 4 of the games she played last week. How many games did she win?

Write an equation to find your answer.

_____ ◯ _____ ◯ _____ 🐢 1.OA.1.1, MP.6.1

Amy won _____ games.

Use precise math language to explain how you know your equation and answer are correct.

_____

_____

_____

_____

Name _____

Another Look! You can make tally marks to show information.
The tally chart shows the ways students get to school.

Getting to School

Car	Walk	School Bus
IIII	||||| II	||||| |||||

You can count the tally marks by 1s and 5s.

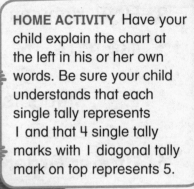

I equals 1 and ||||| equals 5.

___4___ students go by car.

___7___ students walk.

___10___ students ride the bus.

___21___ students in all go to school.

HOME ACTIVITY Have your child explain the chart at the left in his or her own words. Be sure your child understands that each single tally represents 1 and that 4 single tally marks with 1 diagonal tally mark on top represents 5.

Use the tally chart to answer each question.

Balloons 🎈

Red	Blue	Green
|||||	||||| II	II

1. Which color balloon has the most tally marks?

   _____

2. How many balloons are there in all?

   _____ balloons

A first grade class voted on their favorite colors. Answer each question about the tally chart.

Favorite Colors

Blue	Red	Green
丬Ⅱ	川	丬Ⅰ

3. How many students like red?

_____ students

4. How many students like green?

_____ students

5. How many students voted in all?

_____ students

6. Higher Order Thinking Write and answer another question about the tally chart shown above.

_____

_____

_____

_____

_____

7. 🔵 **Assessment Practice** Use the tally chart above. Which two sentences are true? 🔵 I.MD.3.4

☐ 3 students chose green.

☐ 7 students chose blue.

☐ The colors blue and green have the same number of votes.

☐ Red has the least votes.

Name _____

Another Look! The data in a tally chart can be used to complete the picture graph.

Draw pictures to show how many students like to collect shells, stamps, and coins.

Favorite Items to Collect

Shells	Stamps	Coins
🐚	🏳	🪙

Favorite Items to Collect

The graph shows that most students like to collect stamps.

How many students like to collect coins? __4__ students

HOME ACTIVITY Make a tally chart titled Favorite Fruit. Show 4 tally marks next to Apples, 6 tally marks next to Bananas, and 3 tally marks next to Cherries. Have your child make a picture graph to illustrate the data. Then ask him or her questions about the information in the picture graph such as, "Which fruit is the least favorite?"

Use the data in the picture graph to solve each problem.

1. Write the items in order from the favorite item to the least favorite item.

_____ _____ _____

favorite   least
                      favorite

2. The graph shows that ____ students in all like to collect shells, stamps, or coins.

Use the picture graph to solve each problem below.

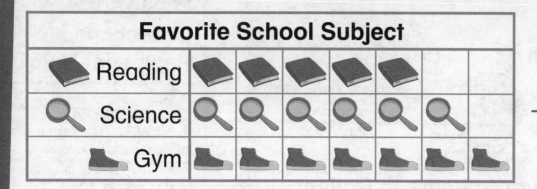

Favorite School Subject

📘 Reading	📘	📘	📘	📘	📘		
🔍 Science	🔍	🔍	🔍	🔍	🔍	🔍	
👟 Gym	👟	👟	👟	👟	👟	👟	👟

3. How many students voted for reading as their favorite subject? _____ students

4. Which is the favorite school subject? _____

5. **Higher Order Thinking** Write a question that can be answered by the picture graph. Then write an equation to match your question.

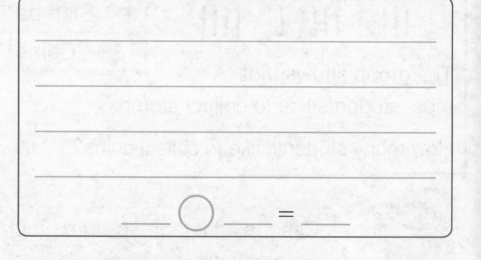

_____

_____

_____

_____

_____ ◯ _____ = _____

6. 🪶 **Assessment Practice** How many students voted for Science? 🪶 I.MD.3.4

5   6   7   13
Ⓐ   Ⓑ   Ⓒ   Ⓓ

7. 🪶 **Assessment Practice** How many students voted in all? 🪶 I.MD.3.4

18   17   12   11
Ⓐ   Ⓑ   Ⓒ   Ⓓ

Name _____

Another Look! Ms. Olson asked her students a survey question. She put tally marks in the tally chart to show the data.

Use the data in the tally chart to complete the picture graph.

Stickers We Like

Moon	Flower	Star
II	ЦЫ II	ЦЫ I

Picture graphs can show the data in a different way.

Stickers We Like

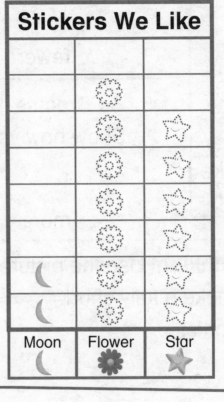

Moon	Flower	Star

HOME ACTIVITY Draw a 2-column picture graph. Label one column "Heads" and the other column "Tails." Then have your child flip a penny. Have him or her record 10 flips in the picture graph. Talk about the results.

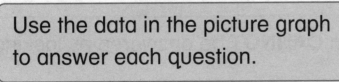
Use the data in the picture graph to answer each question.

1. Which sticker is the least favorite?

   _____

2. Write the stickers in order from favorite to least favorite.

   _____   _____   _____
   favorite   least
                       favorite

3. How many more students like the star than the moon?

   _____ students

What We Like to Do on a Trip

Swim	Hike	Bike

4. Be Precise How many fewer people like to ride a bike than swim? Show how you added or subtracted to find the answer.

____ ◯ ____ = ____

____ fewer

5. Be Precise How many more people like to swim than hike? Show how you added or subtracted to find the answer.

____ ◯ ____ = ____

____ more

6. Higher Order Thinking Use the picture graph above to make a tally chart. Show the tally marks.

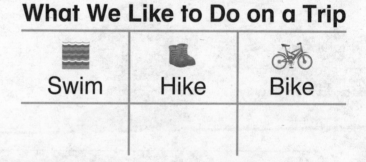

What We Like to Do on a Trip

Swim	Hike	Bike

7. **Assessment Practice** Which question **CANNOT** be answered by looking at the picture graph from Items 4 and 5? 1.MD.3.4

Ⓐ How many more people like to swim than ride a bike?

Ⓑ How many people like to dance?

Ⓒ How many fewer people like to hike than ride a bike?

Ⓓ How many people voted?

Name _____

Another Look! You can use a picture graph to solve problems.

Adam asks 13 friends whether they like butter or jelly on their toast.

How many students' responses does he have left to record?

How Do You Like Your Toast?							
Butter	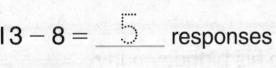						
Jelly							

There are 8 pictures on the graph.

If I start at 8, I need to count up 5 more to get to 13.

$13 - 8 = \underline{5}$ responses

HOME ACTIVITY Create a tally chart to record data about some items in your home. Ask your child to make a picture graph to represent the data in your scenario. Ask your child, "Which category has the most responses? How many in all?" Then ask your child to come up with a different scenario for recording data.

Fill in the missing tally marks. Then use the chart to solve the problem.

1. Maggie asks 12 members of her family for their favorite kind of cereal. 4 people say they like Corny Cones. The rest say they like Great Granola.

   How many people said they liked Great Granola?

   _____ people

Corny Cones	Great Granola
IIII	

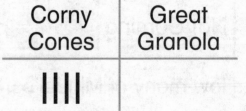

2. Reasoning Lindsay asks her friends whether they like recess or gym more.

How many friends took the survey? _____ friends

Recess	Gym
卌 卌	卌 II

3. Higher Order Thinking Write a problem that can be solved using this picture graph.

_____

_____

Flowers in the Garden							
Roses	🌹	🌹	🌹	🌹	🌹		
Daisies	🌼	🌼	🌼	🌼	🌼	🌼	🌼

4. Assessment Practice Miguel asks 16 friends to come to his birthday party. He makes a graph to show who is coming and who is not.

Birthday Party											
Coming	😊	😊	😊	😊	😊	😊					
Not Coming	😞	😞	😞								

How many of Miguel's friends have not responded yet? Write an equation to solve. I.MD.3.4

_____ ◯ _____ ◯ _____   _____ friends

Name _____

Another Look! 9 students answer a survey about their favorite pet.

4 students vote for dog. 3 students vote for fish.

The rest of the students vote for cat.

How many students vote for cat? Complete the picture graph to show the results of the survey.

2 students chose cat as their favorite pet.

What strategies can you use to solve the problem?

Favorite Pet

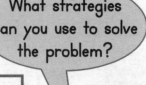

$9 = 4 + 3 + \underline{\ ?\ }$

$9 = 7 + \underline{2}$

HOME ACTIVITY Along with your child, think of a survey question to ask friends or family members. For instance, "Do you prefer grapes, bananas, or pineapples?" Record the results of your survey in a tally chart. Think of some questions about the data, such as, "How many more people chose bananas than grapes?" Have your child write an equation to solve the problem.

Use the picture graph above to answer the question.

I. 4 more students take the survey. Now cat has the most votes and fish has the fewest votes. Use pictures, words, or equations to explain how the 4 students voted.

_____

Snack Time

Phil asks friends to choose their favorite snack.

The tally chart at the right shows the results.

Favorite Snack

Pretzels	Yogurt
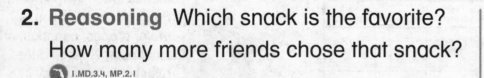	
IIII	IIII IIII

2. **Reasoning** Which snack is the favorite? How many more friends chose that snack?

   I.MD.3.4, MP.2.1

   _____

   _____

3. **Model** How many of Phil's friends answered the survey? Write an equation to show your thinking.   I.OA.I.I, I.MD.3.4, MP.4.1

   _____

   _____

4. **Make Sense** Phil adds grapes as a third choice in his survey. He asks the same friends to answer the survey again. The new survey results are shown in the tally chart at the right. How did the votes change? Use pictures, words, or equations to explain.   I.MD.3.4, MP.I.I

Favorite Snack

Pretzels	Yogurt	Grapes
III	IIII I	IIII

_____

_____

Name _____

 Practice Video Tools Games

Another Look! You can use ten-frames to count groups of 10.

The ten-frame shows 1 group of 10.

You can count the ten-frames by 10s.

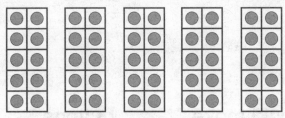

10   20   30   40   50

50 is 5 groups of 10.

50 is fifty.

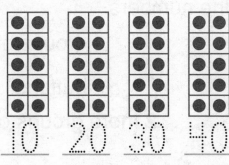

10   20   30   40

40 is __4__ groups of 10.

40 is _forty_____.

HOME ACTIVITY Have your child practice counting by 10s to 120. Then ask questions such as, "How many 10s make 50? What number does 3 groups of 10 make?"

 Count by 10s. Write the numbers and the number word.

1.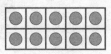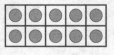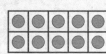

_____ _____ _____ _____ _____ _____ _____

_____ is _____ groups of 10.   _____ is _____.

Count by 10s. Write each missing number.

2. _____, 20, _____, _____, 50, _____ | 3. 70, _____, 90, _____, _____, _____

4. 50, _____, _____, _____, 90, _____ | 5. _____, _____, 50, _____, _____, 80

6. **Higher Order Thinking** Circle groups of 10.
Then count by 10s and write the numbers.

_____ groups of 10

_____ buttons

2 more groups of 10 would make _____ buttons.

7. **Assessment Practice** Jen buys
2 bags of marbles. Each bag has
10 marbles. Count how many marbles
Jen buys. I.NBT.2.2.c

2   12   20   22
Ⓐ   Ⓑ   Ⓒ   Ⓓ

8. **Assessment Practice** Mike has
4 boxes of crayons. Each box has
10 crayons. Count how many crayons
Mike has. I.NBT.2.2.c

4   10   14   40
Ⓐ   Ⓑ   Ⓒ   Ⓓ

Name _____

Another Look! You can use place-value blocks to count forward by 1s.

1 hundred is equal to 10 tens.

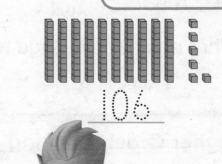

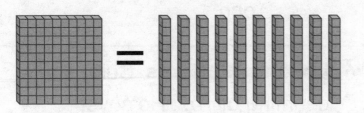

HOME ACTIVITY Say a number between 100 and 105. Have your child count forward by 1s to 120. Repeat with other numbers.

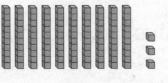
103

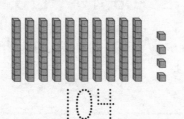
104

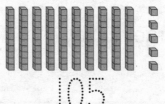
105

106

Start at 103. Count forward to 106.

Count forward by 1s. Write the numbers.

1.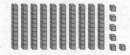
105 _____ _____

2.
_____ 110 _____

3. Start at 118. Count forward. What are the next 2 numbers you will say?

_____ and _____

4. Start at 111. Count forward. What are the next 2 numbers you will say?

_____ and _____

5. Look for Patterns Sage starts counting at 99. She says, "101, 102, 103, 104..."

What number did Sage forget to say?

_____

6. Look for Patterns Cairo starts counting at 107. He says, "108, 109, 110, 112..."

What number did Cairo forget to say?

_____

7. Higher Order Thinking Write the missing numbers in the cards.

Try counting backward to find the number before 103.

| _____ | _____ | 103 | _____ | 105 |

| _____ | 108 | _____ | 110 |

8. 🐦 **Assessment Practice** Which shows the correct order for counting forward by 1s? Choose two that apply. 🐦 1.NBT.1.1

☐ 99, 101, 102, 103

☐ 111, 112, 113, 114

☐ 116, 117, 119, 120

☐ 108, 109, 110, 111

Name _____

Another Look! You can use a number chart to count forward.

1	2	3	4	5	6	7	8	9	10
11	12	13	14	15	16	17	18	19	20
21	22	23	24	25	26	27	28	29	30
31	32	33	34	35	36	37	38	39	40
41	42	43	44	45	46	47	48	49	50
51	52	53	54	55	56	57	58	59	60
61	62	63	64	65	66	67	68	69	70
71	72	73	74	75	76	77	78	79	80
81	82	83	84	85	86	87	88	89	90
91	92	93	94	95	96	97	98	99	100
101	102	103	104	105	106	107	108	109	110
111	112	113	114	115	116	117	118	119	120

What number comes after 33? __34__

What number comes after 34? __35__

What number comes after 35? __36__

33, __34__, __35__, __36__

HOME ACTIVITY Write the following series of numbers: 15, 16, _____, 18, _____, 20. Have your child write the missing numbers. If necessary, create a portion of a hundred chart on a sheet of paper for your child to use while filling in the missing numbers. Repeat with other numbers.

Count by 1s. Write the numbers. Use a number chart to help you.

1. 71, _____, _____, _____, _____

2. _____, _____, _____, 101, _____

3. _____, _____, _____, _____, 111

4. _____, _____, 65, _____, _____

5. 40, _____, _____, _____, _____

6. _____, _____, _____, 32, _____

Higher Order Thinking Write the missing numbers. Look for patterns.

7.

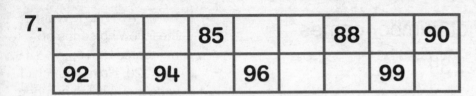

			85			88		90
92		94		96			99	

8.

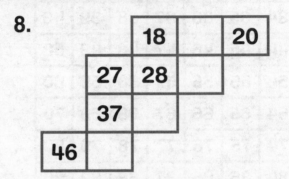

9. ⟳ **Assessment Practice** Draw an arrow to match the missing number to the number chart. ⟳ I.NBT.I.I

92	70	55	31

54		56	57	58	59	60

10. ⟳ **Assessment Practice** Draw an arrow to match the missing number to the number chart. ⟳ I.NBT.I.I

46	33	84	17

81	82	83		85	86	87

© Pearson Education, Inc. 1

Name _____

Another Look! You can count on a number chart. When you count by 10s, the number in the tens digit goes up by one, but the number in the ones digit stays the same.

21	22	23	24	25	26	27	28	29	30
31	32	33	34	35	36	37	38	39	40
41	42	43	44	45	46	47	48	49	50
51	52	53	54	55	56	57	58	59	60
61	62	63	64	65	66	67	68	69	70
71	72	73	74	75	76	77	78	79	80
81	82	83	84	85	86	87	88	89	90
91	92	93	94	95	96	97	98	99	100
101	102	103	104	105	106	107	108	109	110
111	112	113	114	115	116	117	118	119	120

Start at 60. What numbers will you say when you count by 10s?

60, 70, 80, __90__, __100__, __110__, __120__

Start at 25. What numbers will you say when you count by 10s?

25, 35, 45, __55__, __65__, __75__, __85__

HOME ACTIVITY Practice orally counting by 1s and 10s with your child. If necessary, have him or her use a number chart. Ask: "What patterns do you see when you count by 10s?"

Write the numbers to continue each pattern. Use a number chart to help you.

1. Count by 10s.

38, 48, _____, _____, _____, _____

2. Count by 1s.

66, 67, _____, _____, _____, _____

3. Count by 10s.

17, 27, _____, _____, _____, _____

4. Count by 1s.

108, 109, _____, _____, _____, _____

5. Higher Order Thinking Vicky has baseball practice every 10 days. She starts on May 5. Will she have practice on May 19?

Write **Yes** or **No**. _____

How do you know?

_____

_____

Use this calendar to help you!

May

Sunday	Monday	Tuesday	Wednesday	Thursday	Friday	Saturday
	1	2	3	4	5	6
7	8	9	10	11	12	13
14	15	16	17	18	19	20
21	22	23	24	25	26	27
28	29	30	31			

Write 2 more dates that Vicky will have practice.

_____   _____

6. **Assessment Practice** What are the missing numbers? 1.NBT.1.1

65, __?__, __?__, 95, __?__

7. **Assessment Practice** Jamie counts by 1s. He counts: 54, 56, 57, 59. Which numbers did Jamie forget to count?

1.NBT.1.1

_____

© Pearson Education, Inc. 1

Name _____

Another Look! Counting on is like adding.

Start at 87. Count on by 1s to 92.

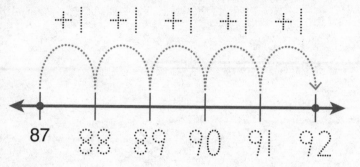

You add 1 each time you count!

HOME ACTIVITY Draw two simple number lines with no labels. Ask your child to use the first number line to count by 1s from 53 to 58. Ask your child to use the second number line to count by 10s from 67 to 107.

Start at 62. Count on by 10s to 112.

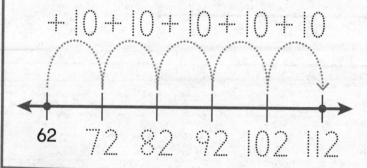

You add 10 each time you count!

Show your counting on the open number line. You can use addition to help.

1. Start at 115. Count on by 1s to 120.

115

2. enVision® STEM There are 16 baby chicks inside a hen house.
Outside, there are 6 more baby chicks. How many baby chicks in all?

3. Start at 18. Count on by 10s to 78.

4. Higher Order Thinking Lorna starts counting at 48.
She counts on by 10s four times.
Then she counts on by 1s three times.
What was the last number she said?
Tell how you know.

5. 🔄 **Assessment Practice** Ben showed part of his counting on this number line.
Fill in the missing numbers. Complete the sentence. 🔄 1.NBT.1.1

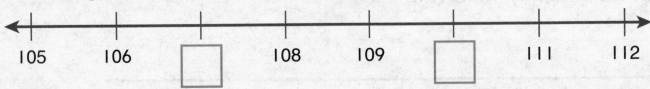

105   106   ☐   108   109   ☐   111   112

Ben counted by _____ from _____ to _____ .

Name _____

Another Look! You can count groups of objects by 1s or 10s.

When you count by 1s, you count each object separately.

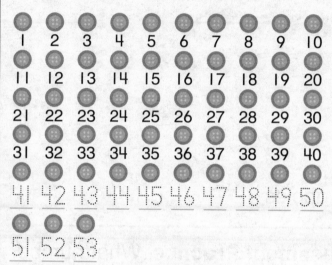

There are ⎯53⎯ buttons.

When you count by 10s, you count groups of 10, and then add the 1s.

There are ⎯53⎯ buttons.

HOME ACTIVITY Set up a pile of between 50 and 120 small objects. Ask your child to count them in the fastest way he or she can think of. Remind your child that sorting the objects into groups or counting more than one at a time will make it easier. Repeat with a different amount between 50 and 120.

 Count the tens and ones. Then write how many in all.

1.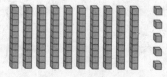

_____ tens _____ ones

_____ in all

2.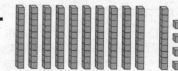

_____ tens _____ ones

_____ in all

3.

_____ tens _____ ones

_____ in all

Count the objects. Show how you counted.
Then write how many in all.

4.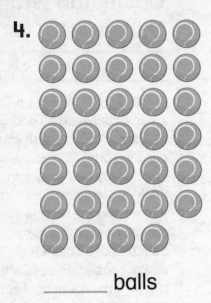

_____ balls

5.

_____ apples

6. Higher Order Thinking Explain why counting by tens might be faster than counting by ones.

_____

_____

7. Assessment Practice What number is shown by the blocks? I.NBT.I.I

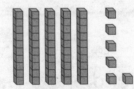

Ⓐ 45

Ⓑ 46

Ⓒ 55

Ⓓ 56

© Pearson Education, Inc. I

Name _____

Another Look! Grouping objects makes it easier to count on.

Amy has some cars in a box and some on the floor.

How can she count to find how many in all?

I can count on from 100.

100 cars

101, 102, 103, 104

I will count by 1s with so few cars. Amy has 104 cars.

HOME ACTIVITY Talk to your child about counting on by 10s and 1s. How can it make things easier? Practice grouping and counting a number of objects, starting from zero and starting from other numbers between 1 and 100.

Generalize and count on by a number to help you find how many in all.

1.

82 dinosaurs

_____ dinosaurs

I counted on by _____.

2.

50 teddy bears

_____ teddy bears

I counted on by _____.

Baby Chicks

Kevin counts 75 chicks in the hen house. He also sees more chicks outside the hen house. How can Kevin count to find how many chicks in all?

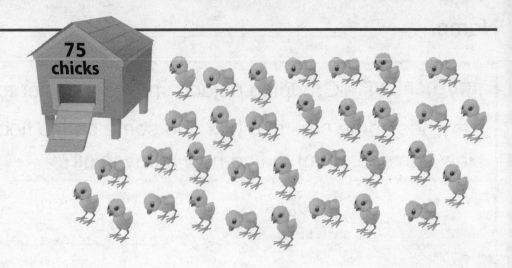

3. Make Sense What do you know about the chicks? What do you need to find?

 MP.1.1

_____

_____

_____

4. Reasoning How do the pictures of the chicks help you? MP.2.1

_____

_____

_____

5. Generalize How many chicks in all? What shortcut did you use to find the answer?

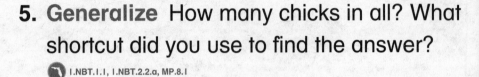 I.NBT.1.1, I.NBT.2.2.a, MP.8.1

_____

_____

_____

_____

_____

_____

_____

Name _____

Another Look! Each number 11 through 19 has 1 ten and some ones.

Write the number of ones for each number.
Then write the number word.

HOME ACTIVITY Write the numbers 11 through 19 on separate index cards. Show one card to your child. Ask him or her to write the number of tens and ones in the number on the other side of the card. Then ask him or her to write the name for the number. After you have worked through all the cards, you will have a set of flashcards that you and your child can save and use for additional practice.

12	16	11
1 ten and _2_ ones	1 ten and _6_ ones	1 ten and _1_ one
twelve	_sixteen_	_eleven_

Write the missing words or numbers.

1. _____

[14] is 1 ten and 4 ones.

2. fifteen

[ ] is 1 ten and 5 ones.

3. nineteen

[ ] is 1 ten and 9 ones.

4. thirteen

[13] is 1 ten and 3 _____.

5. _____

$\boxed{17}$ is 1 ten and 7 ones.

6. eighteen

$\boxed{18}$ is 1 _____ and 8 ones.

7. Algebra $10 + \underline{} = 16$

8. Algebra $12 = \underline{} + 2$

9. Higher Order Thinking Choose a number from 15 through 19. Draw a picture to show how to make the number with ten-frames. Write the number and the number word.

number: _____

number word: _____

10. **Assessment Practice** Match the numbers on the left with the number word on the right. I.NBT.2.2.a, I.NBT.2.2.b

10 and 9   thirteen

1 ten and 0 ones   nineteen

1 ten and 2 ones   eleven

10 and 3   ten

1 ten and 1 one   twelve

Name _____

Additional Practice 8-2
Numbers Made with Tens

Another Look! You can count by tens to find the number of cubes.

The tens digit tells how many groups of 10 there are!

6 tens

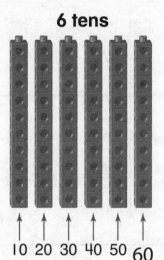

↑ ↑ ↑ ↑ ↑ ↑
10 20 30 40 50 60

7 tens

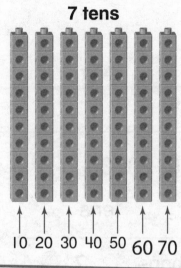

↑ ↑ ↑ ↑ ↑ ↑ ↑
10 20 30 40 50 60 70

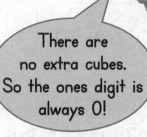

There are no extra cubes. So the ones digit is always 0!

HOME ACTIVITY Say a number of tens (from 1 ten to 9 tens) and ask your child to tell you how many that is in all. For example, 2 tens is 20.

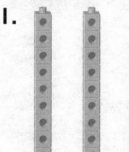

Count to find how many tens.

1.

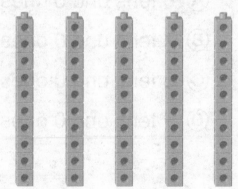

_____, _____, _____, _____, _____, _____, _____, _____

_____ tens and _____ ones

2.

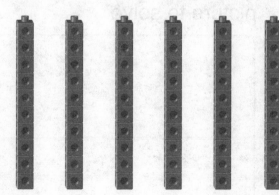

_____, _____, _____, _____, _____, _____, _____, _____, _____

_____ tens and _____ ones

3.

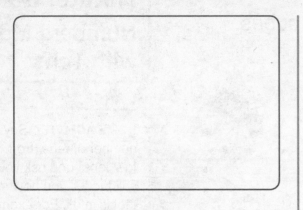

10, 20, 30, 40, 50, 60, 70

_____ tens

4.

10, 20, 30

_____ tens

5.

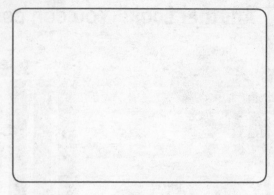

10, 20, 30, 40, 50, 60

_____ tens

---

6. Higher Order Thinking May has 5 bags. Each bag has 10 marbles in it. There are no marbles outside the bags. How many marbles does May have in all? Draw a picture to solve.

May has _____ marbles.

7. **Assessment Practice** Jerry buys a notebook that has 90 pages. Which of the following can represent 90 pages?

I.NBT.2.2.c

Ⓐ 6 tens and 0 ones

Ⓑ 7 tens and 0 ones

Ⓒ 8 tens and 0 ones

Ⓓ 9 tens and 0 ones

© Pearson Education, Inc. I

Topic 8 | Lesson 2

Name _____

Additional Practice 8-3
Count with Groups of Tens and Ones

Another Look! You can count by 10s and then the leftover 1s.

10　20　30　31　32

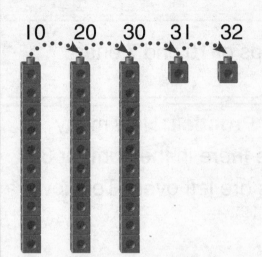

3 groups of 10 and 2 ones

32 in all

10　11　12　13　14

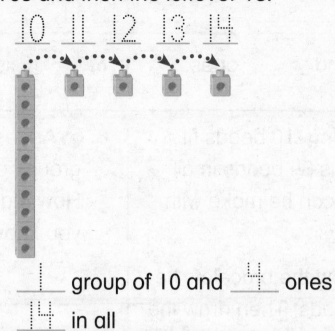

__1__ group of 10 and __4__ ones

__14__ in all

HOME ACTIVITY Place 25 pennies in a pile. Have your child make groups of 10 pennies. Ask, "How many groups of 10 pennies? How many pennies are left over?" Repeat with up to 40 pennies.

 Count by 10s and 1s. Write the numbers.

1. _____

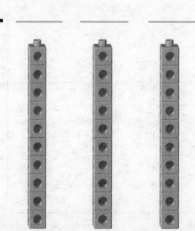

_____ groups of 10

_____ ones

_____ in all

2. _____

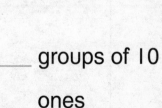

_____ groups of 10

_____ ones

_____ in all

3. _____ is 1 group of 10 and 2 ones.

4. 31 is _____ groups of 10 and 1 one.

5. 14 is 1 group of 10 and _____ ones.

6. _____ is 2 groups of 10 and 7 ones.

7. **Higher Order Thinking** 10 beads fit on a bracelet. Ben has 34 beads in all. How many bracelets can he make with 10 beads on each?

Draw a picture to show the bracelets he can make with his beads. Then draw the beads that will be left over.

8. **Assessment Practice** How many groups of 10 are there in the number 38? How many ones are left over? Tell how you know. I.NBT.2.2

_____

_____

_____

Think about what "left over" means.

© Pearson Education, Inc. 1

Topic 8 | Lesson 3

Name _____

Another Look! You can use a model to show tens and ones.

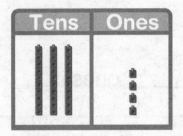

3 tens is 30.

4 ones is 4.

3 tens and 4 ones is 34.

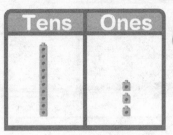

I ten is __10__ .

3 ones is __3__ .

__1__ ten and __3__ ones is __13__ .

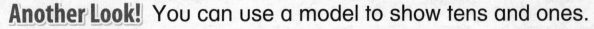

Think about the number of tens and ones.

HOME ACTIVITY Draw 2 squares side by side. Write a 3 in the left square and label it "Tens." Write a 4 in the right square and label it "Ones." Have your child draw a picture to show the number. Ask him or her to use the terms *ones* and *tens* to describe how many.

Count the tens and ones. Then write the numbers.

1.

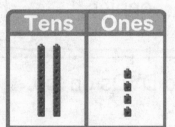

Tens	Ones

_____ tens is _____ .

_____ ones is _____ .

_____ tens and _____ ones is _____ .

2.

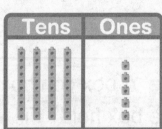

Tens	Ones

_____ tens is _____ .

_____ ones is _____ .

_____ tens and _____ ones is _____ .

Count the tens and ones. Then write the numbers.

3.

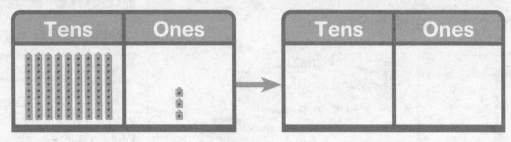

_____ tens and _____ ones is _____ .

4. Reasoning Write the missing number.

6 tens and _____ ones is the same as 60.

5. Higher Order Thinking Sara buys 4 boxes of apples. There are 10 apples in each box. She also buys one bag with 8 apples. How many apples does Sara buy?

Draw a picture to solve the problem.

Sara bought _____ apples.

6. 🏵 **Assessment Practice** A box can hold 4 rows of 10 DVDs and 2 extra DVDs on top. How many DVDs can the box hold? Fill in the missing numbers. 🅣 I.NBT.2.2

_____ tens and _____ ones is _____ .

_____ DVDs

© Pearson Education, Inc. 1

Name _____

Another Look! You can show the tens and ones in a number by drawing a model.

How many tens and ones are in 56?

I count by 10s to 50.
I draw a line for each number I say.
I draw 5 lines.

Then I count by 1s from 50 to 56.
I draw a dot for each number I say.
I draw 6 dots.

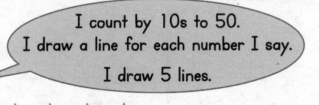

10 20 30 40 50 51 52 53 54 55 56

There are ⁵ tens and ⁶ ones in 56.

HOME ACTIVITY Give your child a number between 0 and 99 and ask him or her to draw a model to represent it. When the model is drawn, ask your child to count by 10s and 1s to show you that the model correctly represents the number. Make sure that he or she points to one line each time when counting by tens and to one dot each time when counting by ones. Repeat with other numbers.

Write the numbers and draw a model to show each number. Count by tens and ones to check.

1.

There are _____ tens and _____ ones in 72.

2.

There are _____ tens and _____ ones in 43.

3.

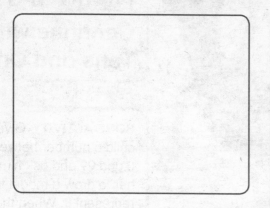

There are _____ tens and _____ ones in 58.

4.

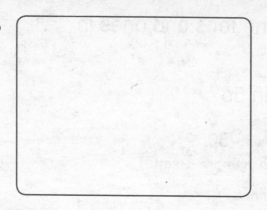

There are _____ tens and _____ ones in 7.

5.

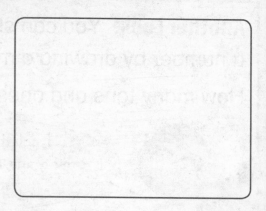

There are _____ tens and _____ ones in 90.

---

6. Higher Order Thinking Haley starts drawing a model for the number 84, but she gets interrupted. Help her finish her model.

7. ⏀ **Assessment Practice** Which number is represented here? ⏀ I.NBT.2.2

Ⓐ 15

Ⓑ 11

Ⓒ 50

Ⓓ 51

Name _____

Another Look! You can break apart a number in different ways.

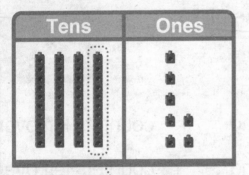

Tens	Ones

47 is 4 tens and 7 ones.

Remember, you can break apart a ten to make 10 ones.

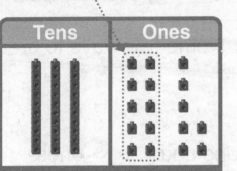

Tens	Ones

47 is _3_ tens and _17_ ones.

HOME ACTIVITY Write a two-digit number. Ask your child to write the number of tens and ones in the number. Then ask your child to use a different way to write the tens and ones in the number. For example, 26 is 2 tens and 6 ones. It is also 1 ten and 16 ones.

Break apart each number in different ways. Use or draw cubes to help.

1. Write two ways to show 24.

   24 is _____ tens and _____ ones.

   24 is _____ tens and _____ ones.

2. Write two ways to show 38.

   38 is _____ tens and _____ ones.

   38 is _____ tens and _____ ones.

Solve each problem.

3. Write a two-digit number. Then break it apart in two different ways.

My number: _____

Way 1: _____ tens and _____ ones

Way 2: _____ tens and _____ ones

4. Look for Patterns Patty has 47 counters. She puts some of them in stacks of 10. Show two ways.

_____ stacks and _____ counters left over

_____ stacks and _____ counters left over

5. A number has 6 tens and 8 ones. What is another way to name the number?

6. Number Sense Name two ways to break apart 50.

Way 1: _____ tens and _____ ones

Way 2: _____ tens and _____ ones

7. Higher Order Thinking What number is shown on the mat?

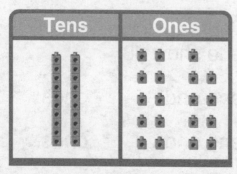

_____

8. ⬤ **Assessment Practice** Which are ways to break apart 32? Choose two that apply.

I.NBT.2.2.d

☐ 2 tens and 3 ones

☐ 3 tens and 2 ones

☐ 3 tens and 12 ones

☐ 2 tens and 12 ones

© Pearson Education, Inc. 1

Name _____

Another Look! You can make a list to solve problems.

What are all the ways you can show 49 as tens and ones?

Tens	Ones
4	9
3	19
2	29
1	39
0	49

Making a list can help you see the pattern and make sure you find all the ways.

HOME ACTIVITY Give your child a two-digit number. Ask, "How many ways can you show the number?" Have him or her make a list of the tens and ones he or she would use to show each way. Continue with several two-digit numbers.

Make a list to solve each problem. You can use cubes to help you.

1. Mark wants to show 34 as tens and ones. What are all the ways?

Tens	Ones

2. Maya wants to show 28 as tens and ones. What are all the ways?

Tens	Ones

Flowers Zach has 53 flowers to plant. He only uses boxes for groups of 10 flowers. Each pot holds only 1 flower.

How many boxes and pots could Zach use to plant the flowers

Zach's List

Boxes	Pots
5	3
4	13
3	23
2	33
1	43

3. **Reasoning** Zach listed how many boxes and pots he could use. Did he list all possible ways? Tell how you know. If Zach missed any ways, list them below. 🐊 MP.2.1

4. **Explain** Is there any way that Zach could plant all 53 flowers using only boxes? Explain how you know. 🐊 1.NBT.2.2.d, MP.3.1

_____

_____

_____

_____

5. **Look for Patterns** How many ways can Zach plant the flowers in boxes and pots? How can you use a pattern to check that you have found all the ways? 🐊 MP.7.1

_____

_____

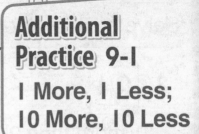
Another Look! You can use place-value blocks to show 1 more than, 1 less than, 10 more than, or 10 less than.

34

You can cross out 1 cube to show 1 less than 34.

1 less than 34 is ___33___.

You can add 1 more cube to show 1 more than 34.

1 more than 34 is ___35___.

You can cross out 1 ten to show 10 less than 34.

10 less than 34 is ___24___.

You can add 1 more ten to show 10 more than 34.

10 more than 34 is ___44___.

HOME ACTIVITY Write a two-digit number. Have your child write the numbers that are 1 more than, 1 less than, 10 more than, and 10 less than the number. Provide pennies as counters if needed. Continue with several two-digit numbers.

Complete each sentence.

1.

1 more than 23 is _____.

1 less than 23 is _____.

2.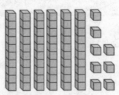

10 less than 68 is _____.

10 more than 68 is _____.

3. 24

I more than 24 is _____.

I less than 24 is _____.

10 more than 24 is _____.

10 less than 24 is _____.

4. 67

I more than 67 is _____.

I less than 67 is _____.

10 more than 67 is _____.

10 less than 67 is _____.

5. Higher Order Thinking Follow the arrows. Write the number that is 1 more, 1 less, 10 more, or 10 less.

You can draw pictures to help you.

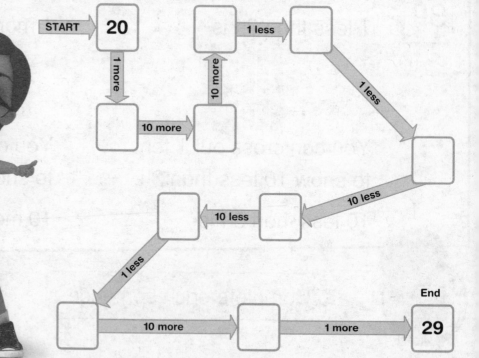

START 20

1 more

10 more

10 more

1 less

1 less

10 less

10 less

10 less

1 less

10 more

1 more

End 29

6. 🦉 **Assessment Practice** Match each number with its description.

I.NBT.3.5

23   1   13   55

10 more than 3   I more than 54   10 less than 33   I less than 2

© Pearson Education, Inc. 1

Topic 9 | Lesson 1

Name _____

Additional Practice 9-2
Find Numbers on a Hundred Chart

Another Look! You can use a hundred chart to find 1 more, 1 less, 10 more, or 10 less than a number.

1	2	3	4	5
11	12	13	14	15
21	22	23	24	25
31	32	33	34	35
41	42	43	44	45

Look at the number in the space after 23 to find 1 more.

1 more than 23 is __24__.

Look at the number in the space before 23 to find 1 less.

1 less than 23 is __22__.

Look at the number 1 row below 23 to find 10 more.

10 more than 23 is __33__.

Look at the number 1 row above 23 to find 10 less.

10 less than 23 is __13__.

What is 1 more, 1 less, 10 more, and 10 less than 23?

HOME ACTIVITY Write a number between 11 and 89 on a sheet of paper. Have your child write the number that is 1 more, 1 less, 10 more, and 10 less than the number. Repeat with several other numbers. Discuss the patterns your child notices.

Use a hundred chart to complete each sentence.

1. 1 more than 77 is _____.

1 less than 77 is _____.

10 more than 77 is _____.

10 less than 77 is _____.

2. 1 more than 62 is _____.

1 less than 62 is _____.

10 more than 62 is _____.

10 less than 62 is _____.

3. 1 more than 89 is _____.

1 less than 89 is _____.

10 more than 89 is _____.

10 less than 89 is _____.

Complete the part of the hundred chart to find I more, I less, 10 more, or 10 less.

4.
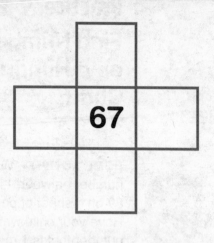

67

5.
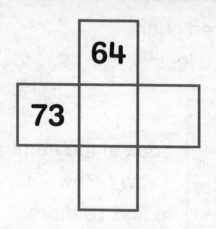

64

73

6.
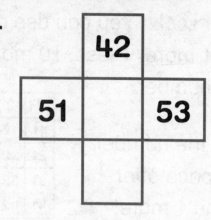

42

51 53

---

7. Higher Order Thinking How can you use place-value blocks and a hundred chart to show the number that is 10 more than 43? What is the number?

8. ⭐ **Assessment Practice** Complete the part of the number chart by finding I more, I less, 10 more, or 10 less. ⬤ I.NBT.3.5

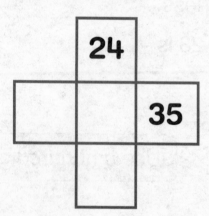

24

35

© Pearson Education, Inc. I

Name _____

Another Look! You can compare numbers to decide if one number is greater than or less than another number.

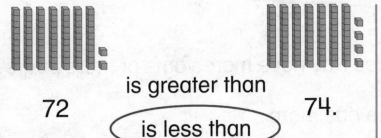

72   is greater than
      (is less than)   74.

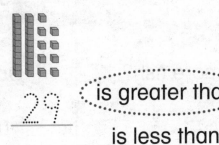

29   (is greater than)   25.
      is less than

Write a number to match each model. Then circle **is greater than** or **is less than**.

1.

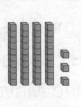

_____ is greater than
_____ is less than .

2.

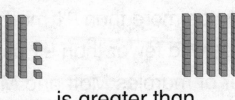

_____ is greater than
_____ is less than .

3.

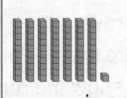 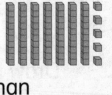

_____ is greater than
_____ is less than .

Solve each problem below. Then complete each sentence.

4. Ty counts 29 fish at the zoo.
He counts 22 birds at the zoo.

Did Ty count more birds or more fish?

He counted more _____ .

_____ is greater than _____ .

5. Kay has 18 yams.
She has 21 pears.

Does Kay have more yams or more pears?

She has more _____ .

_____ is less than _____ .

6. Higher Order Thinking Adam writes a number. The number is greater than 50 and less than 54. What numbers could Adam have written? Explain.

7. Assessment Practice Matt has more than 41 marbles and fewer than 43 marbles.
Maya has more than 47 marbles and fewer than 49 marbles.
Draw lines to show the number of marbles Matt and Maya have. 🕐 I.NBT.2.3

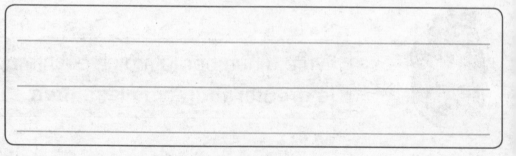

Matt's marbles	40
Maya's marbles	42
	48
	50

Practice Video Tools Games

Additional Practice 9-4

Compare Numbers with Symbols (>, <, =)

Another Look!

You can use < to show that a number is less than another number.
You can use > to show that a number is greater than another number.
You can use = to show that a number is equal to another number.

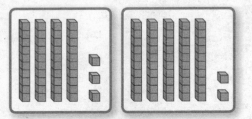

43 < 52

43 is less than 52.

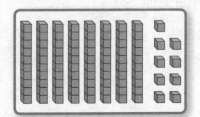

89 > 75

89 is _greater than_ 75.

HOME ACTIVITY Write 2 two-digit numbers. Leave space between the numbers. Have your child write <, >, or = to compare the numbers. Then have him or her read the sentence, replacing the symbol with "is greater than," "is less than," or "is equal to." Repeat with other numbers.

Write >, <, or = to complete the sentence.
Then write **greater than, less than,** or **equal to**.

1.

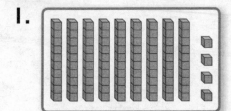

94 ◯ 95

94 is _____ 95.

2.

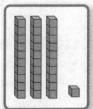

31 ◯ 31

31 is _____ 31.

3. 45 ◯ 50 | **4.** 97 ◯ 97 | **5.** 21 ◯ 12 | **6.** 33 ◯ 63

7. Be Precise Brandon has 79 bottle caps. Gemma has 88 bottle caps. Who has more bottle caps? Write >, <, or = to compare the numbers. Then solve the problem.

Remember to use symbols correctly!

_____ ◯ _____ or _____ ◯ _____

_____ has more bottle caps.

8. Higher Order Thinking Choose 2 numbers. Write 2 different sentences to compare the numbers. Use **is greater than, is less than,** or **is equal to.** Then use >, <, or = .

_____

_____

_____

9. 🐦 **Assessment Practice** Ginny wrote these four sentences for class. Which of Ginny's sentences are **NOT** true? Choose three. 🐦 I.NBT.2.3

☐ 62 < 27

☐ 18 > 24

☐ 42 < 52

☐ 17 = 71

Name _____

Another Look! You can use a number line to compare numbers.

Find a number that is less than 64 and a number that is greater than 64.

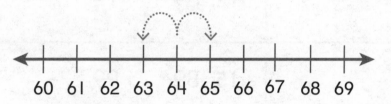

60 61 62 63 64 65 66 67 68 69

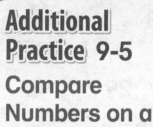

On a number line, numbers to the left are less and numbers to the right are greater!

63 < 64

63 is less than 64.

65 > 64

65 is greater than 64.

Write a number or symbol > or < to make each correct. Use the number line to help you.

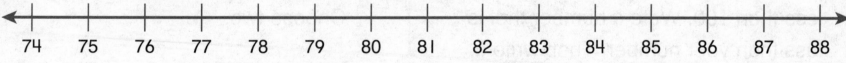

74 75 76 77 78 79 80 81 82 83 84 85 86 87 88

1. _____ < 84

2. 82 > _____

3. 78 < _____

4. 84 ◯ 88

5. 76 ◯ 75

6. 74 ◯ 81

Write > or < to make each correct. Draw a number line to help if needed.

7. 29 ◯ 42 | **8.** 63 ◯ 71 | **9.** 34 ◯ 28

10. 47 ◯ 53 | **11.** 87 ◯ 76 | **12.** 39 ◯ 14

13. 77 ◯ 63 | **14.** 24 ◯ 34 | **15.** 89 ◯ 99

16. Andrew is thinking of a number less than 52 and greater than 40. His number has 3 ones. What is Andrew's number?

_____

17. Model What number is less than 23 and more than 21?

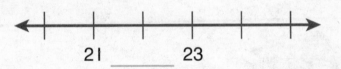

21 _____ 23

18. Higher Order Thinking Choose a number that is greater than 50 and less than 100. Write a number that is less than your number. Then write a number that is greater than your number.

_____ is less than _____.

_____ is greater than _____.

19. 🔵**Assessment Practice** Which numbers are **less than (<)** 79? Choose two. 🔵 I.NBT.2.3

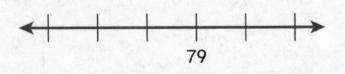

79

75 ☐   78 ☐   80 ☐   81 ☐

Additional Practice 9-6
Make Sense and Persevere

Another Look! Making a list can help you make sense of a problem.

I can use the first clue to make a list of what the answer could be.

Then I can use the second clue to make my list even smaller and find the answer.

82 55 52 47

Ian's number is less than 60.
His numbers could be ___47___,
___52___, and ___55___.

Ian says his number has a 2 in the ones place.
Ian's number is ___52___.

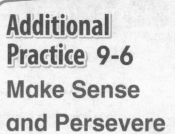

HOME ACTIVITY Tell your child you are thinking of a number. Give clues to help him or her guess, for example "It is greater than 70 and less than 80. It has a 5 in the ones place." Continue with other numbers and clues. Switch roles and have your child think of a number and give you clues.

Make sense of the problems to find the secret numbers from the list below. Show your work.

48   98   62   92

1. Ben's number is less than 90.
His numbers could be

_____.

Ben's number does **NOT** have a 4 in the tens place.

The number is _____.

2. Tim's number is greater than 50.
His numbers could be

_____.

Tim says his number has an 8 in the ones place.

The number is _____.

Numbers in Shapes Jeffrey chooses a secret number from the choices at right. He gives clues to help you find it. What is the secret number?

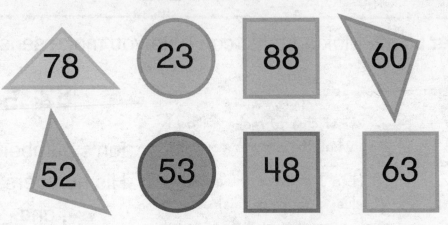

Jeffery's Clues:

- The secret number is **NOT** in a square.
- The number has a 3 in the ones place.
- The number is greater than 50.

3. Make Sense What is your plan for solving this problem? 🔵 MP.1.1

_____

_____

_____

Does your answer fit all the clues?

4. Explain What is the secret number? How do you know your answer is correct? 🔵 I.NBT.2.3, MP.3.1

_____

_____

_____

_____

_____

Secret number: _____

Name _____

Practice Video Tools Games

Additional Practice 10-1
Add Tens Using Models

Another Look! If you know how to add ones, you can add tens.

$40 + 50 = ?$

9 tens is 90.
So, $40 + 50 = 90$.

$40 + 50$ is the same as 4 tens + 5 tens.

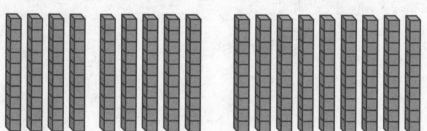

4 tens + 5 tens = 9 tens

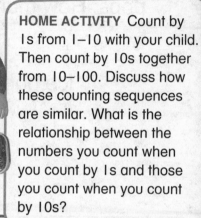

HOME ACTIVITY Count by 1s from 1–10 with your child. Then count by 10s together from 10–100. Discuss how these counting sequences are similar. What is the relationship between the numbers you count when you count by 1s and those you count when you count by 10s?

Write the numbers to complete each equation.

1.

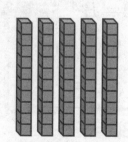

_____ tens + _____ tens = _____ tens

_____ + _____ = _____

2.

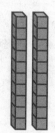 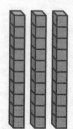

_____ tens + _____ tens = _____ tens

_____ + _____ = _____

Topic 10 | Lesson 1   Go Online | PearsonRealize.com   one hundred thirty-seven **137**

3. Make Sense Carl and Tina buy some boxes of ice pops. Carl buys 3 boxes. Tina buys 4 boxes. Each box has 10 ice pops. How many ice pops did they buy?

_____ + _____ = _____

_____ ice pops

4. Make Sense Rebecca and Brian each have 4 packs of batteries. Each pack has 10 batteries. How many batteries do Rebecca and Brian have in all?

_____ + _____ = _____

_____ batteries

5. Higher Order Thinking Explain how solving $8 + 2$ can help you solve $80 + 20$.

_____

_____

_____

_____

6. Assessment Practice Which equation matches the picture? 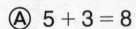 I.NBT.3.4

Ⓐ $5 + 3 = 8$

Ⓑ $50 + 30 = 80$

Ⓒ $50 + 3 = 53$

Ⓓ $5 + 30 = 35$

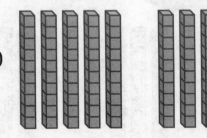

Practice   Video   Tools   Games

Another Look! You can mentally add 10 to any number.

$34 + 10 =$ _____

Imagine moving down 1 square on a hundred chart.

21	22	23	24	25	26	27	28	29	30
31	32	33	34	35	36	37	38	39	40
41	42	43	44	45	46	47	48	49	50

Or add 1 to the tens digit.

3 + 1 = 4, so 3 tens + 1 ten = 4 tens. The ones digit stays the same.

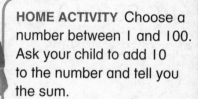

HOME ACTIVITY Choose a number between 1 and 100. Ask your child to add 10 to the number and tell you the sum.

$34 + 10 =$ 44

Use mental math to solve each equation.

1. $55 + 10 =$ _____

2. $10 + 10 =$ _____

3. $83 + 10 =$ _____

4. $16 + 10 =$ _____

5. $15 + 10 =$ _____

6. $36 + 10 =$ _____

Use mental math to solve each problem below.

7. $22 + 10 = $ _____

8. $47 + 10 = $ _____

9. $78 + 10 = $ _____

10. $58 + 10 = $ _____

11. $14 + 10 = $ _____

12. $59 + 10 = $ _____

13. $85 + 10 = $ _____

14. $52 + 10 = $ _____

15. $38 + 10 = $ _____

16. Higher Order Thinking Ms. Frank's class has had 63 different spelling words. On Tuesday, they get some more words.

Now the class has had 73 words. How many spelling words did the class get on Tuesday?

_____ words

17. 🦢 **Assessment Practice** Match each pair of addends with their sum. 🦢 I.NBT.3.5

75	$28 + 10$
64	$65 + 10$
38	$19 + 10$
47	$54 + 10$
29	$37 + 10$

© Pearson Education, Inc. 1

Name _____

Another Look! You can use a hundred chart to add 2 two-digit numbers.

24 + 30 = ?

Start at 24.

Move down 3 rows to add 30.

You stop at ⟋54⟍ .

So, 24 + 30 = ⟋54⟍ .

1	2	3	4	5	6	7	8	9	10
11	12	13	14	15	16	17	18	19	20
21	22	23	24	25	26	27	28	29	30
31	32	33	34	35	36	37	38	39	40
41	42	43	44	45	46	47	48	49	50
51	52	53	54	55	56	57	58	59	60
61	62	63	64	65	66	67	68	69	70
71	72	73	74	75	76	77	78	79	80
81	82	83	84	85	86	87	88	89	90
91	92	93	94	95	96	97	98	99	100

HOME ACTIVITY Use a hundred chart. Give your child a one-digit number, such as 7. Have him or her add a multiple of 10, such as 30. Repeat with other one-digit numbers and other two-digit numbers.

Use a hundred chart to add.

1.   10
       + 36
       _____

2.   15
       + 8
       _____

3.   20
       + 58
       _____

4.   11
       + 40
       _____

5.   40
       + 13
       _____

6.   7
       + 34
       _____

7. Number Sense 5, 15, _____, 35, _____

8. Number Sense 9, _____, 29, 39, _____

9. Higher Order Thinking Mike has 8 marbles. He buys some more. Now he has 28 marbles. How many marbles did Mike buy?

Draw a picture to solve.

Mike bought _____ marbles.

Use the hundred chart to solve each problem.

1	2	3	4	5	6	7	8	9	10
11	12	13	14	15	16	17	18	19	20
21	22	23	24	25	26	27	28	29	30
31	32	33	34	35	36	37	38	39	40
41	42	43	44	45	46	47	48	49	50
51	52	53	54	55	56	57	58	59	60
61	62	63	64	65	66	67	68	69	70
71	72	73	74	75	76	77	78	79	80
81	82	83	84	85	86	87	88	89	90
91	92	93	94	95	96	97	98	99	100

10. Assessment Practice Which equations are **NOT** true? Choose two. I.NBT.3.4

☐ $1 + 10 = 11$ ☐ $8 + 60 = 78$

☐ $3 + 70 = 73$ ☐ $8 + 40 = 84$

11. Assessment Practice Which is the missing addend? I.NBT.3.4

$6 + \underline{\ ?\ } = 76$

Ⓐ 70 Ⓒ 10

Ⓑ 60 Ⓓ 7

Another Look! You can use different strategies to find 30 + 29 on a number line.

Start with 30. Add tens. Then add ones.

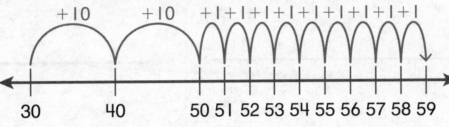

Start with 29. Add tens.

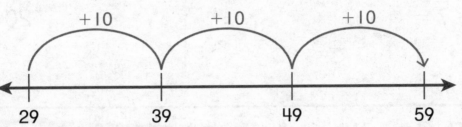

You can start with the number that makes it easier to add on the number line.

$30 + 29 = \underline{59}$

HOME ACTIVITY Draw a blank number line on a piece of paper. Give your child an addition equation involving a two-digit number and a one-digit number and ask him or her to add the equation using the number line.

Add using the number lines.

1. $80 + 18 = \underline{\hspace{1cm}}$

2. $60 + 24 = \underline{\hspace{1cm}}$

3. Count on by 1s to solve $42 + 7$.

$42 + 7 =$ _____

4. Count on by 5s to solve $20 + 25$.

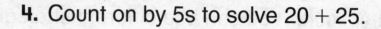

$20 + 25 =$ _____

---

5. Higher Order Thinking Why isn't counting on by 1 the fastest way to add $20 + 26$ on a number line?

_____

_____

---

6. 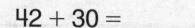**Assessment Practice** Solve $42 + 30$ on an open number line. Show your work. I.NBT.3.4

$42 + 30 =$ _____

Practice | Video | Tools | Games

Another Look! Drawing tens and ones can help you add.

The lines are tens and the dots are ones!

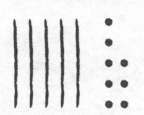

$50 + 8 = \underline{58}$

$23 + 6 = \underline{29}$

HOME ACTIVITY Give your child a multiple of 10, such as 50. Have him or her add a one-digit number such as 4. Repeat with other multiples of 10 and one-digit numbers.

Add. Draw blocks to show your work.

1.

$20 + 2 = \underline{\hspace{1cm}}$

2.

$45 + 30 = \underline{\hspace{1cm}}$

3. Andy has 19 markers. He gets 21 more markers. How many markers does Andy have now?

_____ = _____ + _____

_____ markers

4. enVision® STEM Ted counts 30 stars one night. Another night, he counts 5 stars. How many stars did Ted count in all on both nights?

_____ = _____ + _____

_____ stars

Write the missing number for each problem.

5. Algebra

$70 + $ _____ $ = 76$

6. Algebra

_____ $ + 8 = 28$

7. Algebra

$50 + 3 = $ _____

8. Higher Order Thinking Jon has 4 pencils. He gets more from friends. Now he has 24 pencils. How many pencils did Jon get from friends? Draw a picture to solve.

_____ pencils

9. ✿ **Assessment Practice** Find the missing number. ⬤ I.NBT.3.4

$$71 + \underline{\ ?\ } = 77$$

Ⓐ 6   Ⓑ 10

Ⓒ 60   Ⓓ 70

Name _____

Practice   Video   Tools   Games

Additional Practice 10-6
Make a Ten to Add

Another Look! You can draw place-value blocks to find $24 + 8$.

Sometimes, you can make a 10 when you add.

$24 + 8$
$24 + 6 + 2$

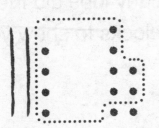

There are 3 tens and 2 ones.

$30 + 2 = \underline{32}$

So, $24 + 8 = \underline{32}$.

HOME ACTIVITY Ask your child to use pennies to find the sum of $26 + 5$. Have your child make groups of 10 to explain the answer.

 Draw blocks and make a 10 to add.

1. $47 + 7$

Think: $47 + \underline{\quad} = 50$

So, break apart 7 into $\underline{\quad} + \underline{\quad}$.

$50 + \underline{\quad} = \underline{\quad}$ So, $47 + 7 = \underline{\quad}$.

2. $55 + 6$

Think: $55 + \underline{\quad} = 60$

So, break apart 6 into $\underline{\quad} + \underline{\quad}$.

$60 + \underline{\quad} = \underline{\quad}$ So, $55 + 6 = \underline{\quad}$.

Topic 10 | Lesson 6   Go Online | **PearsonRealize.com**   one hundred forty-seven **147**

Solve each problem below.

3. **Use Tools** Susy has 16 pennies.
She finds 6 more pennies.
How many pennies does Susy have now?
Draw blocks to show your work.

_____ pennies

4. **Use Tools** Hank drives 26 laps.
Allie drives 7 laps.
How many laps did they drive in total?
Draw blocks to show your work.

_____ laps

5. **Higher Order Thinking** Explain how to find $35 + 9$.
Use equations to show your thinking.

_____

_____

_____

_____

6. **Assessment Practice** Explain how to use the make 10 strategy to find $9 + 27$. I.NBT.3.4

_____

_____

_____

_____

Name _____

Another Look! Find 28 + 27.

You can draw blocks to help you add.

First add the ones.

$8 + 7 = 15$

15 has 1 ten and 5 ones.

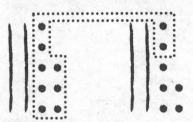

Then add the tens.

$20 + 20 + 10 = 50$

Add the rest of the ones.

$50 + 5 = 55$

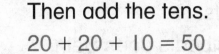

There are 5 tens and 5 ones.

So, $28 + 27 = 55$.

Add. Draw blocks or a number line to help.

1. Find 42 + 17.

$2 + 7 =$ _____

$40 + 10 =$ _____

$42 + 17 =$ _____

2. Find 33 + 28.

$3 + 8 =$ _____

$30 + 20 =$ _____

$33 + 28 =$ _____

3. Reasoning Seth collects model sailboats.
He has 34 large boats.
He has 26 small boats.
How many model sailboats does Seth have in all?
Write an equation to show the problem.

_____ sailboats

4. Reasoning Maria claps 15 times.
Then she claps 22 more times.
How many times does she clap in all? Write an equation to show the problem.

_____ times

5. Higher Order Thinking Write two addends that you will **NOT** need to make a 10 to add. Then solve.

_____ + _____ = _____

6. Assessment Practice For which addition equations can you make a 10 to add? Choose two that apply. $I.NBT.3.4$

☐ $24 + 14 = \underline{\quad?\quad}$

☐ $17 + 25 = \underline{\quad?\quad}$

☐ $16 + 13 = \underline{\quad?\quad}$

☐ $26 + 14 = \underline{\quad?\quad}$

Name _____

Another Look! You draw blocks to find $34 + 18$.

Can you make a 10?

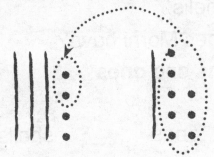

There are __5__ tens.

There are __2__ ones.

$34 + 18 = 52$

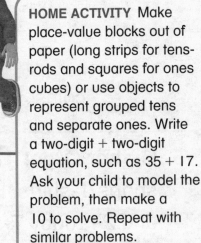

Yes, I can make a 10!

HOME ACTIVITY Make place-value blocks out of paper (long strips for tens-rods and squares for ones cubes) or use objects to represent grouped tens and separate ones. Write a two-digit + two-digit equation, such as $35 + 17$. Ask your child to model the problem, then make a 10 to solve. Repeat with similar problems.

Find each sum. Solve any way you choose. Draw or explain what you did.

1.

$49 + 14 =$ _____

2.

$56 + 10 =$ _____

3. Reasoning Selena has 27 silver coins. She has 30 copper coins. How many coins does Selena have in all?

_____ coins

4. Vocabulary Marni collects shells.
She has 33 gray shells.
She has 37 white shells.
How many shells does Marni have?
Write how many **tens** and **ones**.

_____ tens _____ ones _____ shells

5. Higher Order Thinking Edgar collects sports T-shirts. He has 16 soccer T-shirts and 24 rugby T-shirts. He has 12 hats. How many T-shirts does Edgar have in all? Draw a picture and write an equation to show your work.

_____ T-shirts

6. Assessment Practice Oscar uses place-value blocks to show $67 + 29$. Which of the following model this problem? Choose two that apply. I.NBT.3.4

© Pearson Education, Inc. 1

Name _____

Another Look!

Justin has a box with 24 crayons.
He finds another box with
13 crayons and puts all the
crayons together.

How many crayons does he
have in all? Solve and write
the equation.

You can use drawings to show the problem. Add the tens. Then add the ones.

$$24 + 13 = 37$$

HOME ACTIVITY Write number stories in which two quantities are added together. Ask your child to model each story using a picture and then write an equation to match.

Use drawings to show and solve the problem.
Then write the equation.

1. There are 31 cards in a pile.
   Julie places another 15 cards on the pile.
   How many playing cards are in the pile now?

   _____ + _____ = _____ cards

Coin Collection

Gail, Claire, and Todd each have
their own coin collection.

2. Model Gail has 10 coins. Claire
gives Gail 24 coins. Now how many
coins does Gail have in all? 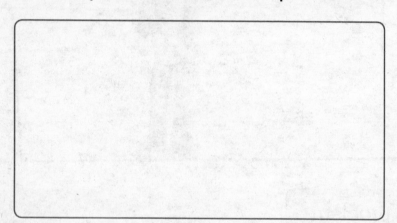 I.NBT.3.4, MP.4.1

Draw a picture to show the problem.

3. Reasoning Write an equation that
matches the story. MP.2.1

_____ ◯ _____ = _____

Draw pictures
to model your
work!

4. Explain Todd says that he can make
10 if he adds 32 coins to 28 coins.
Is he correct?

Explain how you know using words or
pictures. I.NBT.3.4, MP.3.1

Write an equation to find the sum.

_____ ◯ _____ = _____

_____ coins

© Pearson Education, Inc. 1

Name _____

Another Look! If you know how to subtract ones, you can subtract tens.

$40 - 20 = ?$

$40 - 20$ is the same as 4 tens − 2 tens.

4 tens − 2 tens = 2 tens

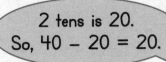

2 tens is 20.
So, $40 - 20 = 20$.

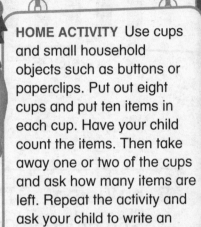

HOME ACTIVITY Use cups and small household objects such as buttons or paperclips. Put out eight cups and put ten items in each cup. Have your child count the items. Then take away one or two of the cups and ask how many items are left. Repeat the activity and ask your child to write an equation to show how many items are left.

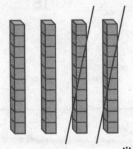

$40 - 20 = \underline{20}$

Cross out the blocks as needed to solve.

1.

_____ tens − 3 tens = _____ ten

_____ − _____ = _____

2.

_____ tens − 2 tens = _____ tens

_____ − _____ = _____

Cross out the blocks as needed and solve the problems.

3.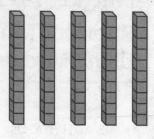

_____ tens − 3 tens = _____ tens

_____ − _____ = _____

4.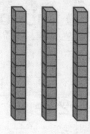

_____ tens − 1 ten = _____ tens

_____ − _____ = _____

5. **enVision® STEM** Meg makes a tool to crush cans. She has 70 cans.
She crushes 20 cans. How many cans does Meg still need to crush?
Write an equation. Then solve.

_____ − _____ = _____ cans

6. **Higher Order Thinking** Write and solve
a story problem for 80 − 50.

_____

_____

_____

_____

7. **Assessment Practice** Which is
equal to 7 tens − 3 tens? ⚫ I.NBT.3.6

Ⓐ 20

Ⓑ 30

Ⓒ 40

Ⓓ 50

Name _____

Another Look! You can use a hundred chart to subtract tens.

50 − 30 = ?

30 is ___3___ tens

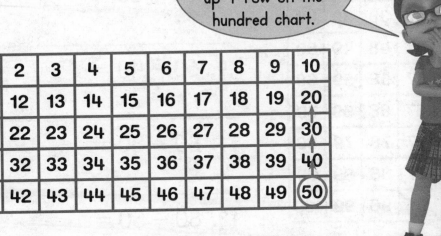

For every ten I take away, I move up 1 row on the hundred chart.

1	2	3	4	5	6	7	8	9	10
11	12	13	14	15	16	17	18	19	20
21	22	23	24	25	26	27	28	29	30
31	32	33	34	35	36	37	38	39	40
41	42	43	44	45	46	47	48	49	50

50 − 30 = ___20___

HOME ACTIVITY Practice counting forward and backwards by 10s with your child. Try counting only some of the sequence and then having your child pick up where you left off. You can also try alternating numbers with him or her.

Use the partial hundred chart to solve each problem. Be ready to explain your work.

41	42	43	44	45	46	47	48	49	50
51	52	53	54	55	56	57	58	59	60
61	62	63	64	65	66	67	68	69	70
71	72	73	74	75	76	77	78	79	80

1. 80 − 30 = _____

2. 70 − 10 = _____

3. 80 − 20 = _____

4. 60 − 10 = _____

1	2	3	4	5	6	7	8	9	10
11	12	13	14	15	16	17	18	19	20
21	22	23	24	25	26	27	28	29	30
31	32	33	34	35	36	37	38	39	40
41	42	43	44	45	46	47	48	49	50
51	52	53	54	55	56	57	58	59	60
61	62	63	64	65	66	67	68	69	70
71	72	73	74	75	76	77	78	79	80
81	82	83	84	85	86	87	88	89	90
91	92	93	94	95	96	97	98	99	100

5. $20 - 10 =$ _____

6. $90 - 30 =$ _____

7. $80 - 30 =$ _____

8. $80 - 40 =$ _____

9. $60 - 40 =$ _____

10. $70 - 20 =$ _____

11. $80 - 80 =$ _____

12. $20 - 20 =$ _____

13. $80 - 50 =$ _____

14. $90 - 20 =$ _____

---

15. Higher Order Thinking Use a hundred chart to solve the problem. Then explain how you got your answer.

$$90 - 80 =$$ _____

_____

_____

16. ✎ **Assessment Practice** Ms. Rodin had 30 spelling tests to grade. Then she graded 10 of them.

How many spelling tests does she have left to grade? 🐊 I.NBT.3.6

Ⓐ 10

Ⓑ 20

Ⓒ 30

Ⓓ 40

Name _____

Another Look! You can use an open number line to subtract.

Find 90 − 50.

Start by marking 90 on the number line.

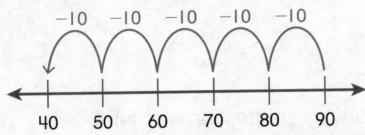

Count back by tens until you have subtracted 50.

What number did you land on? __40__

Since you are counting back, 90 should be on the right side.

HOME ACTIVITY Give your child the following subtraction problems to solve: 20 − 10, 90 − 30, 80 − 50, and 30 − 30. First, ask your child to draw an open number line and solve each problem. If he/she struggles, help by drawing the open number line or marking the first number on the number line.

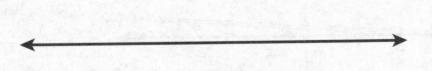

Use number lines to subtract. Be ready to explain your work.

1.

80 − 40 = _____

2.

70 − _____ = 10

3.

$$40 - 30 = \underline{}$$

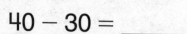

4. Higher Order Thinking Write an equation that shows subtraction with tens. Show the problem on the open number line and solve.

$$\underline{} - \underline{} = \underline{}$$

5. Assessment Practice Find $90 - 40$. Explain your work. I.NBT.3.6

Name _____

Another Look! You can use addition to subtract 10s.

$90 - 50 = ?$ Picture a piece of a hundred chart.

$50 + \underline{40} = 90$, so

$90 - 50 = \underline{40}$.

41	42	43	44	45	46	47	48	49	50
51	52	53	54	55	56	57	58	59	60
61	62	63	64	65	66	67	68	69	70
71	72	73	74	75	76	77	78	79	80
81	82	83	84	85	86	87	88	89	90

If I start on 50, I have to move down 4 to get to 90.

HOME ACTIVITY Practice counting by 10s with your child. Start counting at a multiple of 10 and have him or her continue the sequence. Then practice adding different multiples of 10 (10–90 only).

Use addition to solve each subtraction problem. Use the hundred chart above to help, if needed.

1. $50 + \underline{\hspace{1cm}} = 70$, so

$70 - 50 = \underline{\hspace{1cm}}$.

2. $60 + \underline{\hspace{1cm}} = 90$, so

$90 - 60 = \underline{\hspace{1cm}}$.

Use addition to solve each subtraction problem.
Draw a picture to show your thinking.

3. $20 +$ _____ $= 40$, so $40 - 20 =$ _____.

4. $30 +$ _____ $= 80$, so $80 - 30 =$ _____.

5. $60 +$ _____ $= 70$, so $70 - 60 =$ _____.

6. $40 +$ _____ $= 90$, so $90 - 40 =$ _____.

7. **Higher Order Thinking** Jackie plans to paint the fingernails of 8 friends. She finishes painting 4 of her friends' nails. If each friend has ten nails to paint, how many nails does Jackie still need to paint?

Write and solve an equation to show how many more nails Jackie needs to paint.

_____ $-$ _____ $=$ _____

_____ nails

8. **Assessment Practice** Which addition equation could you use to help you solve the subtraction problem below? ⚡ I.NBT.3.6

$70 - 20 = ?$

Ⓐ $20 + 10 = 30$

Ⓑ $70 + 20 = 90$

Ⓒ $20 + 50 = 70$

Ⓓ $10 + 10 = 20$

© Pearson Education, Inc. 1

Name _____

Another Look! You can mentally subtract 10 from any number.

$72 - 10 = ?$

Imagine moving up 1 row on a hundred chart.

51	52	53	54	55	56	57	58	59	60
61	62	63	64	65	66	67	68	69	70
71	72	73	74	75	76	77	78	79	80

Or, subtract 1 from the tens digit.

$7 \text{ tens} - 1 \text{ ten} = 6 \text{ tens}$

The ones digit stays the same.

$72 - 10 = \underline{62}$

HOME ACTIVITY Give your child a 2-digit number and ask him or her to mentally subtract 10 from it. Have your child explain how he or she found the answer. Repeat with other 2-digit numbers.

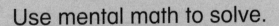

Use mental math to solve.

1. $85 - 10 = \underline{\hphantom{000}}$

2. $37 - 10 = \underline{\hphantom{000}}$

3. $59 - 10 = \underline{\hphantom{000}}$

4. $41 - 10 = \underline{\hphantom{000}}$

5. $75 - 10 = \underline{\hphantom{000}}$

6. $16 - 10 = \underline{\hphantom{000}}$

Use mental math to solve.

7. $29 - 10 =$ _____

8. $14 - 10 =$ _____

9. $28 - 10 =$ _____

10. $45 - 10 =$ _____

11. $78 - 10 =$ _____

12. $13 - 10 =$ _____

13. Algebra Write the missing number in each equation.

$$\boxed{} + 10 = 50 \qquad 50 - \boxed{} = 40 \qquad 70 - 10 = \boxed{}$$

14. Higher Order Thinking Choose two numbers from the list below and write them on the correct lines to make the equation true.

25 34 45 55 68 72

_____ $- 10 =$ _____

15. **Assessment Practice** Draw lines. Match the problems on the left with the numbers on the right. I.NBT.3.5

$49 - 10 =$ _____   6

$85 - 10 =$ _____   39

$16 - 10 =$ _____   51

$61 - 10 =$ _____   75

Name _____

Another Look! You can use addition to solve subtraction problems.

$80 - 50 = ?$

Change the subtraction equation to an addition equation.

$50 + ? = 80$

To get to 80, I need to add 10 three times. That is the same as adding 30.

Count up from 50 to find the missing number.

50, _60_ , _70_ , _80_

$50 + \underline{30} = 80$, so $80 - 50 = \underline{30}$.

HOME ACTIVITY Review subtraction facts to 10 with your child. Talk to him or her about how these facts are related to subtracting tens from numbers to 100. Explain that you are simply subtracting a number of tens rather than a number of ones.

Use the number line to solve the subtraction problems.

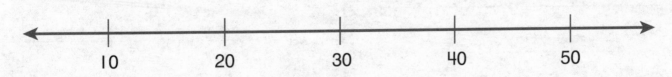

```
        10        20        30        40        50
```

1. $40 - 20 =$ _____

2. $50 - 10 =$ _____

3. $30 - 20 =$ _____

Solve each problem below.

4. Explain Solve 80 − 30 using any strategy you choose. Tell how you solved the problem.

_____

_____

5. Number Sense Write a related addition equation for the subtraction equation below.

$57 - 10 = 47$

_____ + _____ = _____

6. Higher Order Thinking Would you choose to use a hundred chart to solve 90 − 80? Why or why not? If not, which strategy would work better?

_____

_____

_____

_____

7. **Assessment** Explain how you could use a number line to solve 70 − 50.

1.NBT.3.6

_____

_____

_____

_____

Name _____

Another Look! You can use the math you know to solve new problems.

Greg has 30 stickers. He puts 20 stickers into his sticker book. How many stickers does he have left to put away?

Draw a picture:

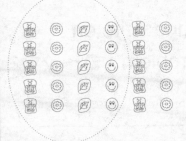

Write an equation:

$$30 - 20 = ?$$

$$30 - 20 = \underline{10}$$

I can model the math in different ways.

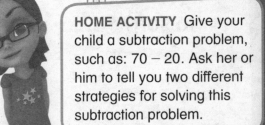

HOME ACTIVITY Give your child a subtraction problem, such as: 70 − 20. Ask her or him to tell you two different strategies for solving this subtraction problem.

Use drawings, models, or equations to solve. Show your work.

1. Jon puts 40 songs onto a playlist. He takes 10 songs off. How many songs are still on the playlist?

2. Tammy sees 24 ants. 10 ants go into an anthill. How many ants are left?

_____ songs

_____ ants

Sock Sorting Jack puts 80 socks in a basket. He sorts 50 socks into one pile.

How many socks does he still need to sort?

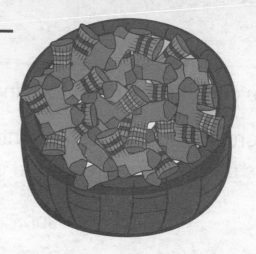

3. **Use Tools** What tool or tools would you choose to use to solve this problem? MP.5.1

_____

_____

_____

4. **Model** Draw a picture and write an equation to solve this problem. 🔵 1.NBT.3.6, MP.4.1

```
┌─────────────────────────────┐
│                             │
│                             │
│                             │
│                             │
│                             │
│    ____ ◯ ____ = ____       │
└─────────────────────────────┘
```

5. **Make Sense** How can you check that your answer makes sense? 🔵 1.NBT.3.6, MP.1.1

_____

_____

Name _____

Additional Practice 12-1
Compare and Order by Length

Another Look! You can describe the lengths of objects by comparing them.

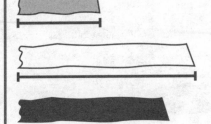

What is the color of the longest ribbon? _White_

What is the color of the shortest ribbon? _Gray_

HOME ACTIVITY Give your child three household objects of different lengths (such as a remote control, a pencil, and a spoon). Ask him or her to put them in order from longest to shortest.

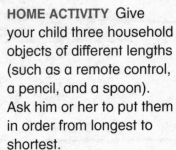

 Write the number of the longest object.
Then write the number of the shortest object.

1. 1: _____

2: _____

3: _____

Longest: ____ Shortest: ____

2. 1:

2:

3:

Longest: ____ Shortest: ____

Topic 12 | Lesson 1   Go Online | PearsonRealize.com   one hundred sixty-nine **169**

Circle the longest object. Cross out the shortest object.

3.

4.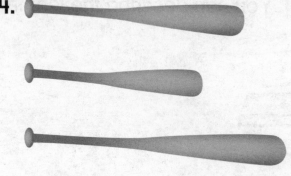

5. Higher Order Thinking Write the order of these 3 objects from longest to shortest:

Car   Bike   Airplane

_____

_____

_____

6. 🐢 **Assessment Practice** Which list shows the order from longest to shortest? I.MD.1.1

1: MATH

2: MATH

3: MATH

Ⓐ Book 1, Book 2, Book 3

Ⓑ Book 2, Book 1, Book 3

Ⓒ Book 2, Book 3, Book 1

Ⓓ Book 3, Book 2, Book 1

Name _____

Another Look! You can compare the lengths of 2 objects without putting them next to each other.

I can use the table to tell if the couch or the desk is longer.

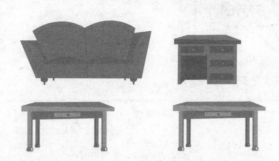

The couch is longer than the table.   The desk is shorter than the table.

That means the couch is <u>longer</u> than the desk.

HOME ACTIVITY Place 3 objects that have different lengths on the table. Point to the object whose length is in the middle. Have your child use the words *longer* and *shorter* to compare each of the other 2 objects to the middle one. Then have your child arrange the 3 objects from longest to shortest.

Circle the picture of the object that is shorter. Use the gray string to help.

1.

_____   _____

2.

_____   _____

Circle the picture of the object that is shorter. Use the gray string to help.

3.

4.

5.

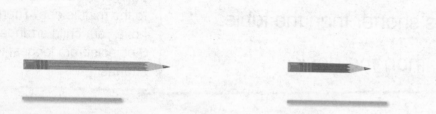

6.

7. Higher Order Thinking Andrea has three candles. Explain how she can use candle B to find out if the candle A is shorter or taller than the candle C.

8. 🐊 **Assessment Practice** Circle the shape that is shorter. Use the gray string to help. 🐊 I.MD.I.I

Name _____

Practice Video Tools Games

Another Look! You can use a ruler to measure length.
To measure to the nearest inch, put one end of the object at the 0 mark.
Look for the number closest to the other end.

HOME ACTIVITY Ask your child to measure a spoon, a candle, and a pencil to the nearest inch. Help your child to use just inch marks to find the nearest inch on the ruler.

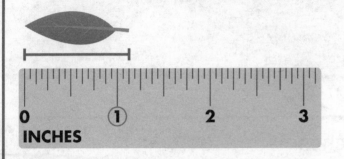

Remember to start at the zero mark.

about ___1___ inch

about ___3___ inches

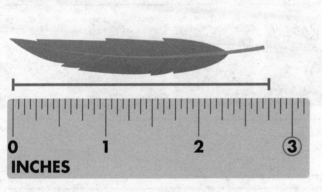

Use a ruler to measure each line to the nearest inch.

1. |—————————————|

about ____ inches

2. |—————————————|

about ____ inches

Use a ruler to measure each object to the nearest inch.

3.

about _____ inch

4.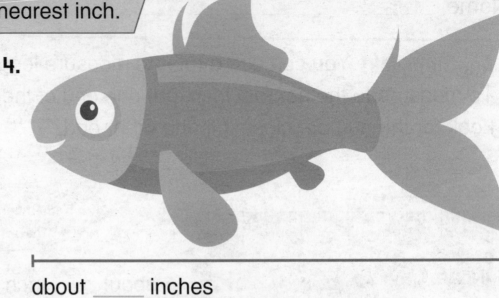

about _____ inches

5. Higher Order Thinking Greg used 1-inch tiles to help him make a ruler. What mistake did he make?

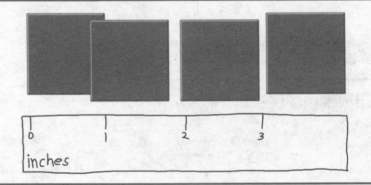

6. Use Tools Carol needs a 2-inch piece of chain. Is this piece the correct length? Circle **Yes** or **No**.

Yes   **No**

7. 🄰 **Assessment Practice** Use a ruler. About how long is the pine cone? 🐟 I.MD.I.a

Ⓐ about 2 inches   Ⓒ about 4 inches

Ⓑ about 3 inches   Ⓓ about 5 inches

Name _____

Another Look! Use string and a ruler to measure the length of the caterpillar.

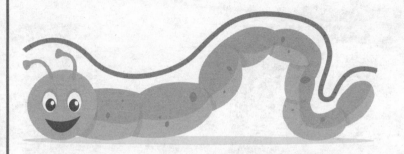

Bend the string to match the caterpillar.

Then straighten the string and measure its length.

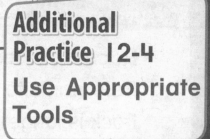

HOME ACTIVITY Draw a curved path on a piece of paper. Have your child measure its length in inches as follows: Fit a piece of string on top of the path. Then straighten the string and use an inch ruler to measure it.

0   1   2   3   4   5
INCHES

The caterpillar is about __5__ inches long.

Circle whether you need just a ruler or string and a ruler to measure each object. Then measure.

1. ruler   string and ruler

about ____ inches

2. ruler   string and ruler

about ____ inches

Race Courses

Pete wants to know which racecar track is longer.

3. **Use Tools** Which tools should Pete use to measure each track to the nearest inch? Should he use the same tools to measure each track? Explain.

1.MD.1.a.a, MP.3.1, MP.5.1

_____

_____

_____

_____

_____

_____

4. **Use Tools** Measure each track. Which track is longer? 1.MD.1.a, MP.5.1

Track 1 is about _____ inches long.

Track 2 is about _____ inches long.

Track _____ is longer.

© Pearson Education, Inc. 1

Name _____

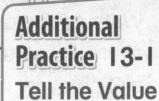
Another Look! Different coins have different values.

Coin	Value	How many in a dollar
penny	1¢	100
nickel	5¢	20
dime	10¢	10
quarter	25¢	4

Remember, the ¢ symbol stands for the word "cents".

Circle every coin worth 10¢. Then write its name.

1.

_____

2. Write a P on every penny, an N on every nickel, a D on every dime, and a Q on every quarter.

3. Draw lines to match each coin with its value.

nickel   10¢

quarter   1¢

penny   25¢

dime   5¢

4. Higher Order Thinking Nina has a dollar's worth of nickels and a dollar's worth of dimes. How many coins does she have in all?

5. ⓕ Assessment Practice Matt wants to buy a toy car that costs a dollar. Which coins can he use? Choose three that apply.   1.MD.2.a.c

☐ 20 nickels

☐ 2 quarters

☐ 10 dimes

☐ 100 pennies

Practice Video Tools Games

Another Look! Use counting to find the value of a group of coins.
Find the value of 5 dimes and 3 pennies.
Start with the coin that is worth more.

10¢ 20¢ 30¢ 40¢ 50¢ 51¢ 52¢ 53¢

In All

53¢

HOME ACTIVITY Place a small group of dimes and pennies on the table. Place some with the heads side up and some with the tails side up. Have your child count to find the total value of the coins. Ask your child to record the value with a cent symbol.

Count on to find each total value.

1.

In All

_____

_____ _____ _____ _____ _____ _____ _____

2.

In All

_____

_____ _____ _____ _____ _____ _____

3. Be Precise Find the total value of the dimes and pennies below.

4. Jack has 23¢. He has dimes and pennies. Draw a picture to show the coins Jack could have.

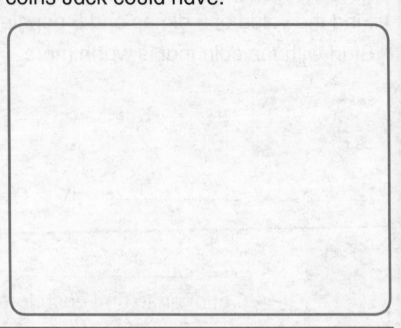

5. Higher Order Thinking Ali wants to buy the headband. She has 6 dimes. How many more cents does she need?

72¢

6. Assessment Practice Which coins have a total value of 27¢? I.MD.2.a.b

Ⓐ 2 dimes and 4 pennies

Ⓑ 3 dimes and 7 pennies

Ⓒ 2 dimes and 7 pennies

Ⓓ 4 dimes and 2 pennies

Practice Video Tools Games

Another Look! You can use the hands on a clock to tell time.

The short hand is the hour hand. The long hand is the minute hand.

minute hand

hour hand

The hour hand points to 6.

The minute hand points to 12.

It is 6 o'clock.

The hour hand points to _3_.

The minute hand points to _12_.

It is _3_ o'clock.

HOME ACTIVITY Using an analog clock in your home, help your child make a list of activities they do on a given day. Have him or her write the time that each activity begins.

Write the time shown on each clock.

1.

hour hand: _____

minute hand: _____

_____ o'clock

2.

hour hand: _____

minute hand: _____

_____ o'clock

3.

hour hand: _____

minute hand: _____

_____ o'clock

 Go Online | PearsonRealize.com

Draw hour hands and minute hands to show the time.

4.

10 o'clock

5.

2 o'clock

6.

11 o'clock

7.

3 o'clock

8.

9 o'clock

9.

6 o'clock

Solve each problem below.

10. Higher Order Thinking Write a good time for eating lunch. Then draw an hour hand and a minute hand to show the time.

_____ o'clock

11. 🐾 **Assessment Practice** Every Saturday, Rachel wakes up after 6 o'clock and before 9 o'clock. Which tells the time Rachel might wake up every Saturday?

🐾 I.MD.2.3

Ⓐ 2 o'clock

Ⓑ 4 o'clock

Ⓒ 5 o'clock

Ⓓ 8 o'clock

© Pearson Education, Inc. 1

Name _____

Another Look! Both clocks show the same time.

4 tells the hour.

00 tells the minutes.

Both clocks show 4 o'clock.

_7_ tells the hour.

_00_ tells the minutes.

Both clocks show _7_ o'clock.

HOME ACTIVITY Use a digital clock in your home to help your child practice telling time. When your child is doing an activity on the hour, ask him or her to tell you the time. Repeat with other times and other activities.

Draw the hands on the clock face.
Then write the time on the other clock.

1.

3 o'clock

2.

7 o'clock

3.

10 o'clock

Draw lines to match the clocks that show the same time.

4.

 1:00    3:00

5.

 12:00    9:00

6.

5:00   6:00

---

7. Higher Order Thinking Write a good time for eating dinner.

_____ o'clock

Draw hands on the clock face to show the time you wrote.
Then write the time on the other clock.

---

8. 🕐 **Assessment Practice** Look at the time on the clock face.
Which clocks below do **NOT** show the same time?
Choose three that apply. 🕐 I.MD.2.3

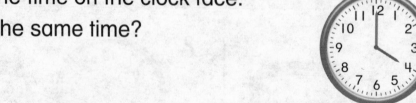

10:00 ☐   8:00 ☐   7:00 ☐   4:00 ☐

Name _____

Another Look! Clocks can tell us the time to the half hour.

A half hour is 30 minutes.

The hour hand is between 7 and 8.
The minute hand is on 6.
It is 7:30.

The hour hand is between ⎯11⎯ and ⎯12⎯.

The minute hand is on ⎯6⎯.
It is ⎯11:30⎯.

HOME ACTIVITY Using an analog clock, have your child practice telling the time to the half hour. If possible, have him or her move the hands on the clock to tell the time you say. For example, say, "Show me 6:30." Have your child write the time on a sheet of paper after telling the time.

Complete the sentences. Then write the time on the other clock.

1.

The hour hand is between ____ and ____.
The minute hand is on ____.
It is _____.

2.

The hour hand is between ____ and ____.
The minute hand is on ____.
It is _____.

3. Explain Vanessa walks to the library and arrives at half past 5.

Write the time on the clock.
Then explain how you solved.

_____

_____

_____

4. Algebra Kirk stirs his soup at 1:00. He started cooking the soup 30 minutes earlier. What time did Kirk start cooking his soup? Draw the hands on the clock face and write the time.

___ : ___

5. Higher Order Thinking Write about something you do a half hour before bedtime. Write the time on the clock. Draw the hands on the clock face to show the time.

_____

_____

6. 🔊 **Assessment Practice** Which shows the same time as the clock face? 🔊 1.MD.2.3

8:30   8:00   7:30   6:30

Ⓐ   Ⓑ   Ⓒ   Ⓓ

Name _____

Another Look! You can use reasoning to solve problems about time.

Mr. K's students can work with a partner for the second half of Writing.

What time can students start working with a partner?

How are the numbers related? How can you use what you know to solve?

Students can start working with a partner at  `1:30` .

Class Schedule	
Time	**Class**
12:30	Silent Reading
1:00	Writing
2:00	P.E.

HOME ACTIVITY Help your child create a schedule for a typical school day. Ask questions about the schedule, such as, "What time do you eat lunch?" or "What time is a half hour after Math?"

> What time is halfway between 1:00 and 2:00? I know 1:00 to 2:00 is 1 hour. I know a half hour is 30 minutes. 30 minutes after 1:00 is 1:30.

Use the schedule above to solve the problems below.

1. Draw the hands on the clock to show when Silent Reading begins.
Then explain your reasoning.

_____
_____

2. What time is it 30 minutes after P.E. starts?
Write the correct time on the clock.
Then explain your reasoning.

_____
_____

Fundraiser Schedule	
Time	**Activity**
10:00	Introductions
10:30	Auction
11:30	Fun Run
2:00	Closing Speech

Fun Run Gina's school is hosting a fundraiser for music programs. Can you use the schedule to help solve problems about the fundraiser?

Use your understanding of telling and writing time to solve the problems.

3. **Model** What time do the introductions start at the fundraiser? Write the correct time on the clock to show your answer. MAFS.1.MD.2.3, MP.4.1

4. **Reasoning** Gina drew the hands on this clock to show the time the Closing Speech starts. Is she correct? If not, draw the correct hands on the clock at the right. MAFS.1.MD.2.3, MP.2.1

Topic 13 | Lesson 6

Another Look! You can define shapes by the number of straight sides and vertices. A shape is closed if the sides are connected.

Tell if the shape is closed or not. Then count the straight sides and vertices.

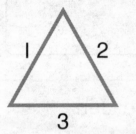
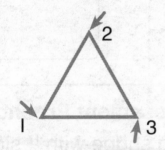

A triangle is a closed shape with 3 straight sides and 3 vertices.

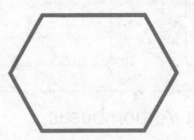

Closed? __Yes__ A hexagon has __6__ straight sides and __6__ vertices.

HOME ACTIVITY Draw a square, a rectangle, a triangle, and a circle. Have your child tell how many straight sides and how many vertices each shape has.

For each shape, tell if it is closed or not. Then tell how many sides and vertices it has.

1.

Closed? _____ A circle has _____ straight sides and _____ vertices.

2.

Closed? _____ This shape has _____ straight sides and _____ vertices.

3.

Closed? _____ A hexagon has _____ straight sides and _____ vertices.

4. Draw a shape with more than 3 sides.

5. Draw a shape with 4 vertices.

6. Draw a shape with no vertices.

7. Higher Order Thinking A rhombus is a closed shape with 4 equal sides and 4 vertices. Circle the shape that is not a rhombus. Explain how you know.

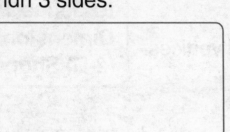

_____

_____

_____

8. 🔊 **Assessment Practice** Jen draws a shape with 4 sides and 4 vertices. Which could be Jen's shape? Choose three that apply.

🟧 I.G.I.I

Practice Video Tools Games

Another Look! You can use certain features to identify shapes.

How can you tell if a shape is a square?

These shapes are all gray. They also all have 4 sides. But only two of them are squares.

These shapes are all different colors and sizes. But they are all squares.

All squares: have 4 equal sides.

are gray.

are small.

have 4 vertices.

HOME ACTIVITY Work with your child to find shapes around the house (such as triangles, squares, and hexagons). Then make lists of defining attributes for each shape. Ask him or her to draw or construct 3 different examples of each shape.

Circle the words that are true for the shape.

1.

All rectangles: are black.

are closed figures.

have 4 sides and 4 vertices.

have 4 square corners.

2.

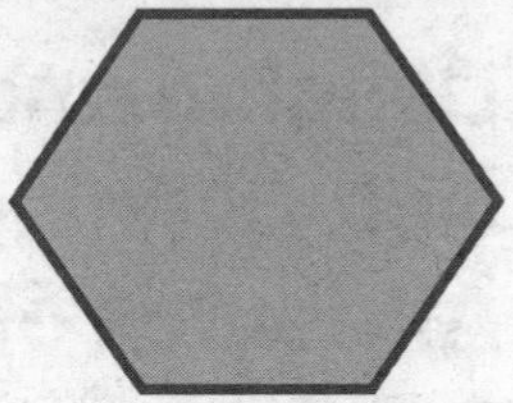

All hexagons: are gray.

have 6 straight sides.

have 6 equal sides.

have 6 vertices.

---

3. Higher Order Thinking Danielle says these shapes are rectangles because they are both tall shapes with 4 straight sides and 4 vertices. Do you agree? Why or why not?

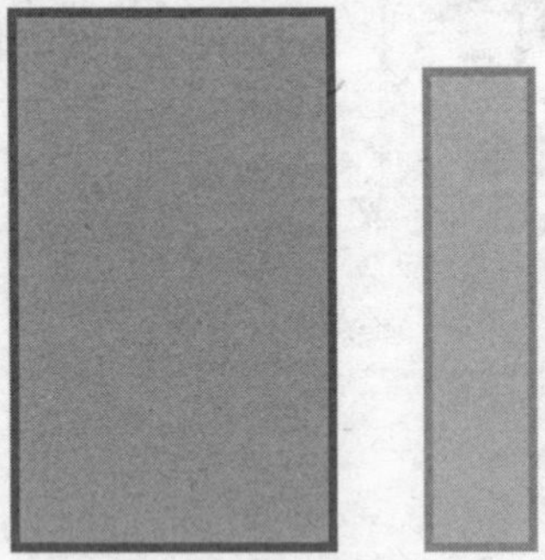

---

4. **Assessment Practice** Which attributes help define a square? Choose three that apply. I.G.I.I

☐ Has 4 square corners   ☐ Has 4 equal sides
☐ Is long and straight   ☐ Is a rectangle

© Pearson Education, Inc. I   **Topic I4** | Lesson 2

Name _____

Another Look! You can use different materials to make shapes.

This circle was made with string.

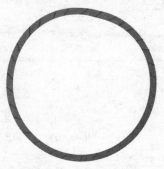

A circle has 0 sides and 0 vertices.

This ___rectangle___ was made with craft sticks.

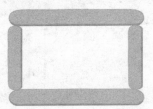

The opposite sides of a ___rectangle___ are equal.

HOME ACTIVITY Have your child use materials you have at home to make different shapes. Have him or her count the number of sides for each shape.

Use materials to make each shape. Glue or tape the shape in the box.

1. Make a triangle. Tell 1 thing about a triangle.

_____

2. Make a square. Tell 1 thing about a square.

_____

Draw a picture to solve each problem below.

3. Lucia made a shape. The shape has 4 sides. The shape has opposite sides that are equal. What shape did Lucia make?

Lucia made a _____.

4. Yani made a shape. The shape has no sides. The shape has no vertices. What shape did Yani make?

Yani made a _____.

5. Higher Order Thinking Use shapes to draw a house. Label each shape you used.

6. 🔵 **Assessment Practice** Lee made a triangle using toothpicks. He knows that a triangle has 3 sides, but does not know how many vertices it has. Circle each vertex on the triangle below. 🔵 I.G.I.1

© Pearson Education, Inc. 1

Name _____

Another Look! You can put shapes together to make new shapes.

You can make a

using 3 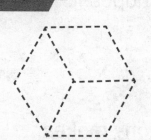 .

You can make a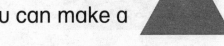

using __3__ ▲ .

HOME ACTIVITY Have your child cut out triangles, squares, and rectangles from old newspapers and magazines. Have him or her use the shapes to make new shapes.

Circle the shapes you can use to make each shape.

1. Make a .

2. Make a  .

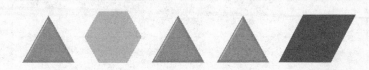

Solve each problem below.

3. Number Sense Write the number of each shape needed to make .

4. Kerry uses these shapes to make a new shape.

Circle the shape Kerry makes.

5. Tony uses these shapes to make a new shape.

Circle the shape Tony makes.

6. Higher Order Thinking Carlos wants to use 3  to make a square. Can he? Explain.

7. 🚩 **Assessment Practice** How many  does Adam need to make a ? 🚩 I.G.I.2

1	2	3	4
Ⓐ	Ⓑ	Ⓒ	Ⓓ

© Pearson Education, Inc. 1

Practice Video Tools Games

Another Look! You can use different blocks to make the same picture.

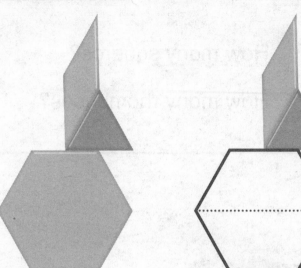

Finish the apple by tracing blocks that make a hexagon without using the hexagon block.

HOME ACTIVITY Ask your child to cut out 2-D shapes such as rectangles, squares, circles, and triangles. Have him or her put the shapes together to make a picture.

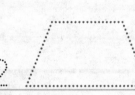

Which shapes did you use? ___2___

Finish the turtle without using triangles.

Draw the top of the shell without drawing a triangle.

1.

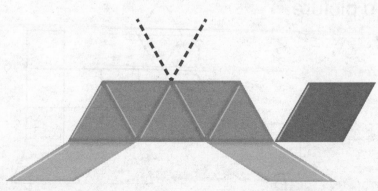

Solve the problems below.

2. Reasoning Write the number of each block used to make this microphone.

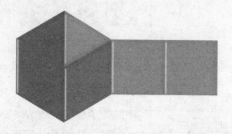

How many triangles? _____   How many squares? _____

How many trapezoids? _____   How many rhombuses? _____

3. Higher Order Thinking What are two different ways to fill in this alligator?

Draw or explain how you know.

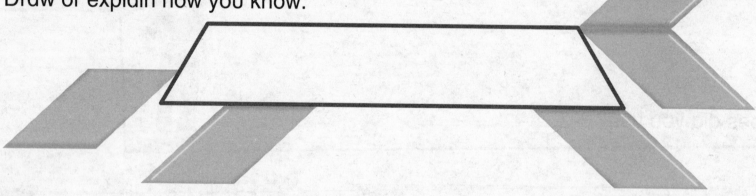

Way 1: _____   Way 2: _____

4. **Assessment Practice** José is making a picture of a bunny. He is missing the matching ear.

Which block is missing? I.G.I.2

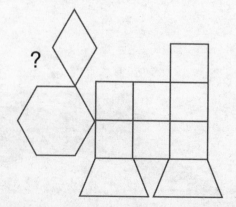

Ⓐ   Ⓑ   Ⓒ   Ⓓ

© Pearson Education, Inc. I

Name _____

Another Look! Flat surfaces, faces, edges, and vertices can be used to describe 3-D shapes.

  flat surface vertex

A cone has 1 flat surface.

A cube has 8 vertices.

A rectangular prism has __6__ faces.

A cylinder has __0__ edges.

HOME ACTIVITY Gather household objects that look like the following 3-D shapes: cube, rectangular prism, sphere, cone, and cylinder. Have your child count the number of faces or flat surfaces, edges, and vertices on each shape. Then have him or her choose 2 shapes and tell how they are alike and different.

Circle the 3-D shape that answers each question.

1. Which 3-D shape has 1 flat surface and 1 vertex?

2. Which 3-D shape has 0 flat surfaces and 0 vertices?

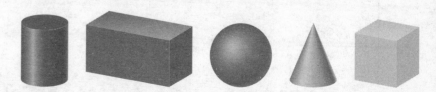

Solve the problems below.

3. 🔤 **Vocabulary** Circle the number of vertices on a **rectangular prism**.

0 vertices   4 vertices   5 vertices   8 vertices

---

4. Circle the shapes that have 6 faces and 12 edges.

5. Circle the shape that has 2 flat surfaces and 0 vertices.

---

6. **Higher Order Thinking** Draw or name two 3-D shapes. Find the total number of vertices and faces or flat surfaces.

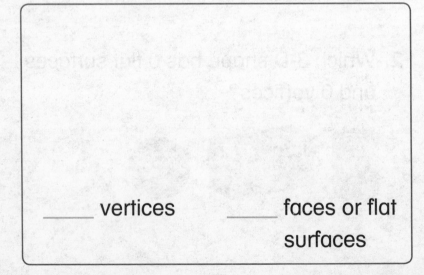

_____ vertices   _____ faces or flat surfaces

7. 🔵 **Assessment Practice** Katie picks two of these 3-D shapes out of a bag. What is the total number of flat surfaces or faces that could be on the shapes she picked? Choose two that apply.   🔵 I.G.1.1

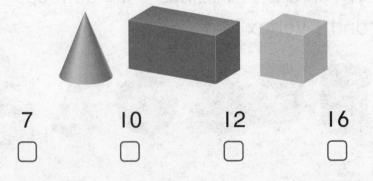

7   10   12   16
☐   ☐   ☐   ☐

Name _____

Another Look! How can you tell if a shape is a cube?

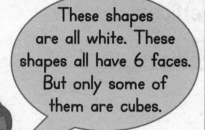

These shapes are all white. These shapes all have 6 faces. But only some of them are cubes.

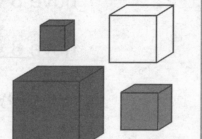

These shapes are all different colors and sizes. But they are all cubes.

So, all cubes:

- have 6 square faces.
- are white.
- have 8 vertices.
- are large.

HOME ACTIVITY Draw or print out pictures of 3-D shapes and ask your child to tell you one attribute of each shape shown.

Circle the words that are true for the shape.

1. **All spheres:**

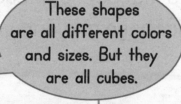

have no flat surfaces.

have 3 flat surfaces.

cannot roll.

are gray.

2. All rectangular prisms: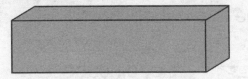

have 6 faces.

have 6 vertices.

have 8 vertices.

are gray.

---

3. Higher Order Thinking Jane says that both of these shapes are cones because they both have one circular base and one vertex.
Do you agree? Why or why not?

_____

_____

---

4. 🔵 **Assessment Practice** Match each shape with the words that describe it. I.G.I.I

cone   rectangular prism   cube   cylinder

12 edges   0 vertices   I vertex   8 vertices

© Pearson Education, Inc. I

Name _____

Another Look! You can combine 3-D shapes to make new shapes.

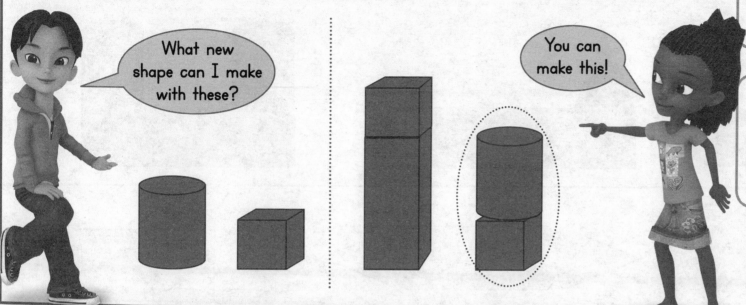

What new shape can I make with these?

You can make this!

HOME ACTIVITY Ask your child to show you how to make a new 3-D shape by using household objects such as shoe boxes, soup cans, and funnels.

Look at the two 3-D shapes. Circle the new shape you can make when combining the shapes.

I.

   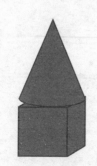   

2.

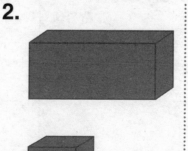      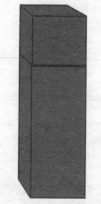

The first two 3-D shapes can be used over and over to make new 3-D shapes. Circle the new shape that could be made by using the first two shapes.

3.

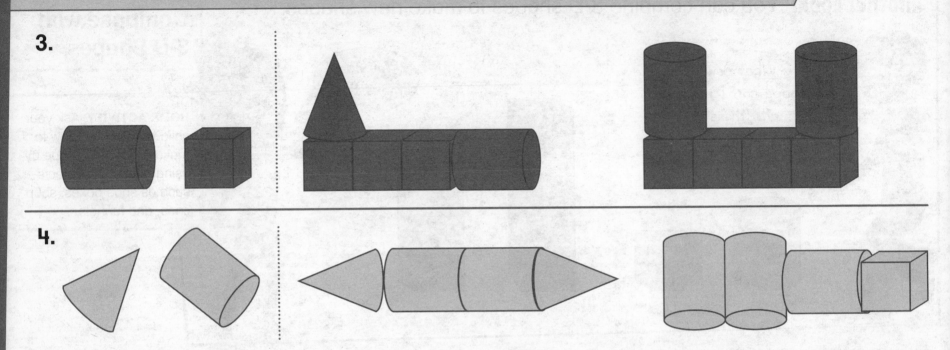

4.

5. Higher Order Thinking Ramon wants to make a rectangular prism with 5 cubes. Can he do this? Explain. Draw cubes to show your answer.

6. 🕎 **Assessment Practice** Which two shapes can be used to make a larger rectangular prism? 🕎 I.G.I.2

Ⓐ

Ⓑ

Ⓒ

Ⓓ

Practice Video Tools Games

Another Look! You can make sense of problems and keep working if you get stuck.

These are rectangles. Circle the words that are true of all rectangles.

All rectangles:

have 4 sides ———→ Count the sides. Are there 4?

are white ———→ Look above at the rectangles. Are all of the shapes white?

have 1 long side ——→ Look at the sides of a rectangle. Is there only 1 long side?

have 4 vertices :——→ Count the vertices. Are there 4?

HOME ACTIVITY Have your child gather examples of spheres and cubes (or any other two 2-D or 3-D combination) Ask: "What is true of all spheres (or another 2-D or 3-D shape)?" Help your child identify attributes of each shape he or she finds.

All of these shapes are rectangular prisms. Circle the words that are true of all rectangular prisms.

1. All rectangular prisms:

are gray   have 12 edges   have 4 faces   have 6 faces

Puzzle Pieces

Laura is sorting her puzzle pieces into like piles. She has triangles, rectangles, squares, circles, and trapezoids. Help her sort the pieces.

2. Be Precise Laura wants to put all shapes with 4 sides into one pile. Use the letters on each shape to tell which shapes would be put in the pile. I.G.I.I, MP.6.I

3. Reasoning Laura wants to put all shapes with at least I vertex in a pile. Use the letters on each shape to tell which shapes would be put in the pile. I.G.I.I, MP.2.I

4. Make Sense Sort shapes A–J into two or more piles based on similarities by drawing or writing. Then explain how you sorted. I.G.I.I, MP.I.I

Name _____

Another Look! A shape can be divided into shares that are equal or shares that are **NOT** equal.

This rectangle is divided into equal shares.

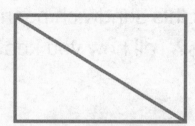

This rectangle is **NOT** divided into equal shares.

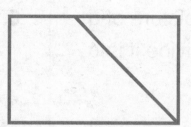

The shares are the same size.
There are 2 equal shares.

The shares are **NOT** the same size.
There are ___0___ equal shares.

HOME ACTIVITY Draw 2 squares, 2 rectangles, and 2 circles. Have your child divide 1 square, 1 rectangle, and 1 circle into equal shares and 1 square, 1 rectangle, and 1 circle into unequal shares.

Write the number of equal shares in each shape.
If the shares are **NOT** equal, write 0.

1.

   _____ equal shares

2.

   _____ equal shares

3.

   _____ equal shares

4.

2 equal shares

5.

4 equal shares

6.

2 equal shares

7. enVision® STEM Draw a picture of a bike wheel. Draw lines to divide it into 4 equal shares.

8. Be Precise Has this sandwich been cut into equal shares? Tell how you know.

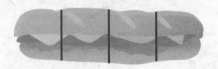

_____

_____

_____

9. Higher Order Thinking Two brothers divide a slice of bread into equal shares. One brother thinks he got a smaller share than the other. How can he check if he is right?

_____

_____

10. **Assessment Practice** Which tells how many equal shares the apple has?

I.G.I.3

Ⓐ 8   Ⓑ 3

Ⓒ 4   Ⓓ 2

© Pearson Education, Inc. I

Name _____

Additional Practice 15-2
Make Halves and Fourths of Rectangles and Circles

Another Look! You can divide shapes into halves and fourths.

Two **halves** make one whole.

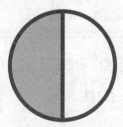

Four **fourths** make one whole.

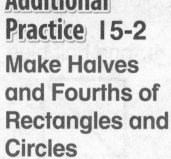
One fourth is the same as one quarter.

Each share is called a **half**.
One **half** of the circle is gray.

Each share is called a fourth.
One fourth of the rectangle is black.
One quarter of the rectangle is white.

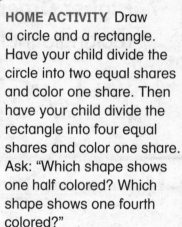

HOME ACTIVITY Draw a circle and a rectangle. Have your child divide the circle into two equal shares and color one share. Then have your child divide the rectangle into four equal shares and color one share. Ask: "Which shape shows one half colored? Which shape shows one fourth colored?"

Circle the correct shapes for each problem.

1. one half gray

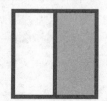 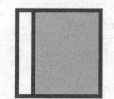

2. one quarter black

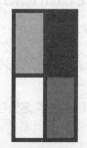 

3. one half white

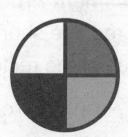 

 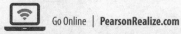

4. one half blue

5. one quarter purple

6. one fourth red

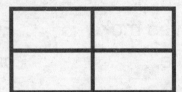

7. Higher Order Thinking Color one half of each circle blue. Color one half of each rectangle that is **NOT** a square orange. Color one quarter of each square red.

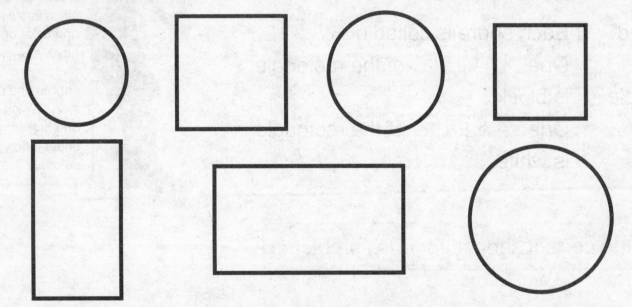

8. 🔵 **Assessment Practice** Sandy divided a rectangle into four equal shares. She colored one share red, one share blue, and two shares yellow. How much of the rectangle did she color red? Choose two that apply. 🔵 I.G.I.3

one half ☐   one quarter ☐   two of four shares ☐   one fourth ☐

© Pearson Education, Inc. 1   **Topic 15** | Lesson 2

Name _____

Another Look! These rectangles are the same size.

The rectangle with more equal shares has smaller shares.

The rectangle with fewer equal shares has larger shares.

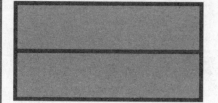

_2_ equal shares

halves

larger equal shares

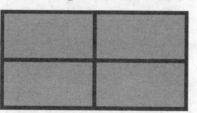

_4_ equal shares

fourths

smaller equal shares

HOME ACTIVITY Draw two circles that are the same size. Ask your child to draw lines to divide one circle into halves and one circle into fourths. Then ask your child which circle has more equal shares and which circle has larger equal shares.

Compare the two shapes. Tell how many equal shares. Then circle **smaller** or **larger** and **more** or **fewer** for each.

1. quarters

equal shares:

smaller   larger

more   fewer

____ equal shares

halves

equal shares:

smaller   larger

more   fewer

____ equal shares

2. Reasoning Ginny and Martha each have a pizza. Their pizzas are the same size.

Ginny cuts her pizza into fourths.
Martha cuts her pizza into halves.

Who has more slices? _____

How many more? _____

Who has larger slices? _____

3.  **Vocabulary** Divide this square into **halves**. Then shade one half of the square.

4. Higher Order Thinking Lucas divides a circle into 2 equal shares. Then he divides each share in half. How many equal shares are there now? What are they called? Use words and pictures to explain.

5. **Assessment Practice** Mary is designing a sign. She wants one half of the sign to be black, one fourth of it to be gray, and one quarter of it to be white.

Which shows what Mary's sign might look like? I.G.I.3

© Pearson Education, Inc. I

Practice   Video   Tools   Games

Another Look! Dale's flag is divided into 4 equal shares. 2 of the shares are gray. The rest are green. How many shares of Dale's flag are green?

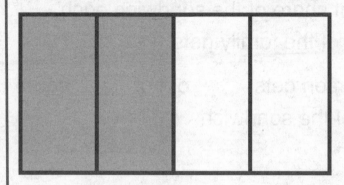

The picture can help you see that the shares that are not shaded must be green.

So, __2__ out of 4 shares will be green.

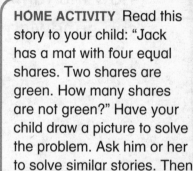

A picture can help you solve the problem. You can use the math words you know to write a sentence to solve the problem.

HOME ACTIVITY Read this story to your child: "Jack has a mat with four equal shares. Two shares are green. How many shares are not green?" Have your child draw a picture to solve the problem. Ask him or her to solve similar stories. Then write a sentence that goes with each number story.

Draw a picture to solve the problem. Then complete the sentences.

1. Sasha's scarf is divided into halves. One of the shares is brown. The rest of the scarf is green.

_____ out of _____ equal shares is brown.

_____ out of _____ equal shares is green.

Sandwich Shares The Dawson family buys 1 big sandwich to share equally. There are 4 members of the family.

2. Model Draw a picture to show how the family members can share the sandwich. 🔵 I.G.I.3, MP.4.1

3. Reasoning Complete the sentence that tells what share of the sandwich each member of the family gets.

Each person gets _____ out of _____ equal shares of the sandwich. 🔵 I.G.I.3, MP.2.1

4. Explain Rachel is a member of the Dawson family. She gives her share of the sandwich to her brother Gary. What share of the sandwich does Gary have now? Explain how you found the answer using words or pictures. 🔵 I.G.I.3, MP.3.1

Nombre _____

La hora y el dinero

Estimada familia:

Su niño(a) está aprendiendo sobre el valor de las monedas y cómo decir la hora. En este tema aprenderá:

- a identificar el valor de las monedas de 1¢, 5¢, 10¢ y 25¢; y a contar el valor de combinaciones de monedas de 1¢ y 10¢;

- a leer la esfera del reloj y decir la hora hasta la media hora y la hora más cercana.

Contar el valor de las monedas

Hallar el valor de un grupo de monedas de 10¢ y 1¢, ayuda a su niño(a) a reforzar lo que aprendió sobre el valor de posición de los números hasta 100.

10¢	20¢	21¢	22¢	23¢

Decir la hora a la hora más cercana

El siguiente reloj indica las 5 en punto.

La manecilla pequeña o de la hora, señala la hora 5. La manecilla larga, o minutero, señala 12, que quiere decir en punto.

Aquí está otro tipo de reloj que indica la hora.

5:00

Indica los números 5 para la hora y 00 para en punto.

Decir la hora

Materiales 2 lápices de diferente longitud o 2 pedazos de pasta seca de espagueti, papel, lápiz

Dibuje un reloj tradicional con los números 1 al 12 y sin manecillas. Dibuje un reloj digital en blanco en otra hoja de papel. Escriba los números 1 al 12, dos 0, y un 3 en diferentes hojas de papel. Haga las manecillas una corta y otra larga usando 2 lápices o 2 pedazos de espagueti seco. Dígale a su niño(a) alguna hora a la hora o la media hora más cercana. Pídale que muestre la hora en el reloj tradicional con el par de manecillas, y que luego muestre la misma hora en el reloj digital. Repita la actividad varias veces.

Observe a su niño(a)

Pídale a su niño(a) que describa cualquier patrón o método abreviado que observe cuando dice la hora. Por ejemplo, pregúntele a su niño(a) qué es verdadero sobre la manecilla de la hora cuando indica las 2:30, 3:30 y 4:30.

Name _____

Time and Money

Dear Family,

Your child is learning about the values of coins and how to tell time. In this topic, he or she will learn:

- to identify the value of pennies, nickels, dimes, and quarters; and count the value of combinations of pennies and dimes;

- to read a clock face and to tell time to the half hour and hour.

Counting the Value of Coins

Finding the value of a group of dimes and pennies helps reinforce what your child has learned about place value of numbers to 100.

| 10¢ | 20¢ | 21¢ | 22¢ | 23¢ |

Telling Time to the Hour

The clock below shows 5 o'clock.

On an analog clock, the short hand, or hour hand, points to the hour of 5. The long hand, or minute hand, points to 12, which stands for "o'clock."

A digital clock, shown below, is another type of clock that shows time.

It shows the numbers 5 for the hour and 00 for "o'clock."

Telling Time

Materials 2 pencils of different lengths or 2 pieces of dry spaghetti, paper, pencil

Draw an analog clock with the numbers 1 to 12 and no hands. Draw a blank digital clock on another piece of paper. Write the numbers 1 to 12, two 0s, and a 3 on separate pieces of paper. Make short and long hands using 2 pencils or 2 pieces of dry spaghetti. Tell your child a time to the hour or half hour. Have him or her show the time on the analog clock with the pair of hands, and then show the same time on the digital clock with the numbers. Repeat the activity several times.

Observe Your Child

Ask your child to describe any patterns or shortcuts he or she notices while telling time. For instance, ask your child what is true about the minute hand at 2:30, 3:30, and 4:30.

Medir longitudes

Estimada familia:

Su niño(a) está aprendiendo a medir la longitud. En este tema, aprenderá a comparar y a ordenar objetos de acuerdo a sus longitudes y a usar una regla para medir objetos a la pulgada más cercana. Estas son destrezas básicas importantes para aprender a medir usando una variedad de unidades estándares.

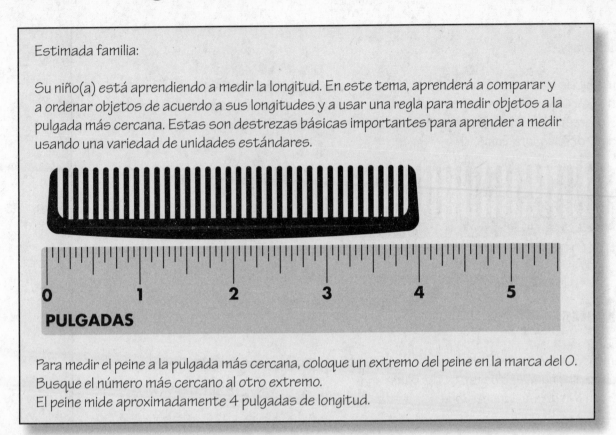

Para medir el peine a la pulgada más cercana, coloque un extremo del peine en la marca del O. Busque el número más cercano al otro extremo.
El peine mide aproximadamente 4 pulgadas de longitud.

Medir longitudes

Materiales 5 objetos pequeños del hogar (cepillo de dientes, linterna, tenedor, etc.), regla de pulgadas

Pídale a su niño(a) que mida la longitud de cada objeto a la pulgada más cercana. Anime a su niño(a) que le diga cada medida usando la palabra *pulgadas.* Por ejemplo, *La linterna mide aproximadamente 6 pulgadas de longitud.*

Observe a su niño(a)

A medida que su niño(a) mide los objetos, recuérdele que debe tener cuidado cuando coloque un extremo del objeto en la marca del 0 de la regla.

Name _____

Measure Lengths

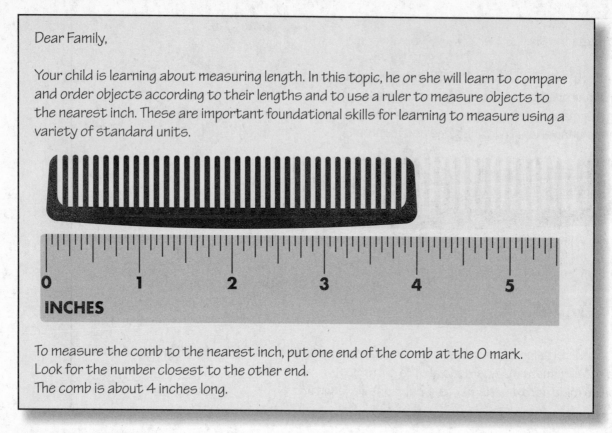

Dear Family,

Your child is learning about measuring length. In this topic, he or she will learn to compare and order objects according to their lengths and to use a ruler to measure objects to the nearest inch. These are important foundational skills for learning to measure using a variety of standard units.

To measure the comb to the nearest inch, put one end of the comb at the 0 mark.
Look for the number closest to the other end.
The comb is about 4 inches long.

Measuring Length

Materials 5 small household objects (toothbrush, flashlight, fork, etc.), inch ruler

Ask your child to measure the length of each object to the nearest inch. Encourage your child to tell you each measurement using the word *inches*. For example, *The flashlight is about 6 inches long.*

Observe Your Child

As your child measures the objects, encourage him or her to be careful about placing one end of the object at the 0 mark on the ruler.

Usar modelos y estrategias para restar decenas

Estimada familia:

Su niño(a) está aprendiendo a restar números de dos dígitos. En este tema, aprenderá destrezas importantes para restar. También aprenderá a usar herramientas como modelos y tablas de 100 para ayudarle a restar. El énfasis en este tema es restar decenas. Hallar la diferencia de 70 − 40 es un ejemplo de cómo restar decenas.

1	2	3	4	5	6	7	8	9	10
11	12	13	14	15	16	17	18	19	20
21	22	23	24	25	26	27	28	29	30
31	32	33	34	35	36	37	38	39	40
41	42	43	44	45	46	47	48	49	50
51	52	53	54	55	56	57	58	59	60
61	62	63	64	65	66	67	68	69	70

El dibujo muestra cómo restar 70 − 40 usando una tabla de 100.

Empiece en 70 y luego halle 10 menos. Haga esto 4 veces porque 40 es lo mismo que 4 decenas.

70 − 40 = 30

Restar decenas

Materiales tabla de 100, 50 fichas o monedas de 1¢

Pídale a su niño(a) que calcule mentalmente para resolver 50 − 30. Luego, pídale que resuelva el mismo problema usando una tabla de 100 y luego usando fichas (o monedas de 1¢). Pídale que explique qué estrategia le gusta más y por qué.

Observe a su niño(a)

Pídale a su niño(a) que explique cómo puede calcular mentalmente para resolver 80 − 40. Usen términos de valor de posición, como *8 decenas menos 4 decenas son 4 decenas.*

Name _____

Use Models and Strategies to Subtract Tens

Dear Family,

Your child is learning to subtract 2-digit numbers. In this topic, he or she will learn important subtraction skills, and how to use tools like models and hundred charts to help him or her subtract. The emphasis in this topic is on subtracting tens. Finding the difference of 70 – 40 is an example of subtracting tens.

1	2	3	4	5	6	7	8	9	10
11	12	13	14	15	16	17	18	19	20
21	22	23	24	25	26	27	28	29	30
31	32	33	34	35	36	37	38	39	40
41	42	43	44	45	46	47	48	49	50
51	52	53	54	55	56	57	58	59	60
61	62	63	64	65	66	67	68	69	70

The picture shows how to subtract 70 – 40 using a hundred chart.

Start on 70 and then find 10 less. Do this 4 times because 40 is the same as 4 tens.

70 – 40 = 30

Subtracting Tens

Materials hundred chart, 50 counters or pennies

Have your child solve 50 – 30 using mental math. Then have him or her solve the same problem using a hundred chart, and then using counters (or pennies). Have your child explain which strategy he or she likes best and why.

Observe Your Child

Have your child explain how she or he can solve 80 – 40 using mental math. Look for place-value terms, such as *8 tens minus 4 tens is 4 tens.*

Usar modelos y estrategias para sumar decenas y unidades

Estimada familia:

Su niño(a) está aprendiendo estrategias para sumar números. Su niño(a) usará una variedad de modelos, incluyendo bloques de valor de posición y tablas de 100. También aprenderá a sumar decenas y unidades usando una recta numérica vacía. Esta es una estrategia importante porque ayuda a su niño(a) a pensar en los números y sus relaciones.

La siguiente recta numérica vacía muestra una manera de sumar $16 + 30$. Empiece en 16 y cuente hacia adelante en decenas. Cada "salto" representa sumar 10.

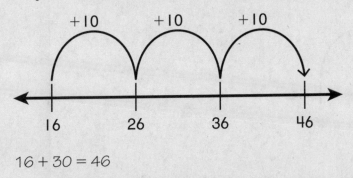

$16 + 30 = 46$

Sumar decenas y unidades

Materiales 8 tarjetas de fichero, papel, lápiz

Escriba uno de los siguientes números en cada tarjeta de fichero: 7, 8, 12, 15, 20, 23, 30, 50. Ponga las tarjetas cara abajo y pídale a su niño(a) que escoja dos tarjetas. Pídale que le muestre una manera de sumar los números de las tarjetas. Repita la actividad pidiéndole a su niño(a) que mezcle las tarjetas y escoja un nuevo par de números para sumarlos.

Observe a su niño(a)

Después de que su niño(a) sume los números de un par de tarjetas de fichero, pídale que compruebe la respuesta usando otro método para sumar. Pídale que describa en qué se parecen los dos métodos y en qué se diferencian.

Name _____

Use Models and Strategies to Add Tens and Ones

Dear Family,

Your child is learning strategies to add numbers. Your child will use a variety of models, including place-value blocks and hundred charts. He or she will also learn to add tens and ones using an open number line. This is an important strategy because it helps your child think about numbers and their relationships.

The open number line below shows one way to add 16 + 30. You start at 16 and count on by tens. Each "jump" represents adding 10.

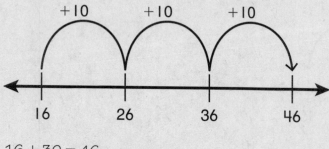

16 + 30 = 46

Adding Tens and Ones

Materials 8 index cards, paper, pencil

Write one of the following numbers on each index card: 7, 8, 12, 15, 20, 23, 30, 50. Place the cards facedown and have your child choose two cards. Ask your child to show you one way to add the numbers on the cards. Repeat the activity by having your child mix the cards and choose a new pair of numbers to add.

Observe Your Child

After your child adds the numbers on a pair of index cards, ask him or her to check the answer by using a different method to add. Ask your child to describe how the methods are similar and how they are different.

Nombre _____

Comparar números de dos dígitos

Estimada familia:

Su niño(a) está aprendiendo a comparar números. Aprenderá a usar una tabla de 100 para mostrar las relaciones de 1 más que, 1 menos que, 10 más que y 10 menos que, de un número dado. Su niño(a) también aprenderá a usar los signos >, < y = para comparar números.

Esta es una parte de una tabla de 100:

Uno más que/menos que
Diez más que/menos que

31	32	33	34	35	36	37	38	39	40
41	42	43	44	45	46	47	48	49	50
51	52	53	54	55	56	57	58	59	60

Puede usar una tabla de 100 para hallar un número que es 1 más que, 1 menos que, 10 más que o 10 menos que un número dado.

Halle el número 42 en la tabla.

Para hallar 1 más que 42, muévase 1 casilla hacia la derecha. 43 es uno más que 42.

Para hallar 1 menos que 42, muévase 1 casilla hacia la izquierda. 41 es uno menos que 42.

Para hallar 10 más que 42, muévase 1 casilla hacia abajo. 52 es diez más que 42.

Para hallar 10 menos que 42, muévase 1 casilla hacia arriba. 32 es diez menos que 42.

Practique hallar más que/menos que un número

Materiales tabla de 100

Pídale a su niño(a) que halle el número 47 en la tabla de 100. Pídale que use la tabla para hallar 1 más, 1 menos, 10 más y 10 menos que 47. Pida a su niño(a) que explique cómo halló las respuestas.

Observe a su niño(a)

A medida que su niño(a) explica cómo halló las respuestas, anímelo(a) a que haga generalizaciones sobre en qué dirección moverse en la tabla para hallar los números que son más o menos. Por ejemplo: "Me muevo hacia arriba y a la izquierda para hallar números que son menos".

Name _____

Compare Two-Digit Numbers

Dear Family,

Your child is learning to compare numbers. He or she will learn to use a hundred chart to show the relationships of 1 more than, 1 less than, 10 more than, and 10 less than a given number. Your child will also learn to use the symbols >, <, and = to compare numbers.

Here is part of a hundred chart:

31	32	33	34	35	36	37	38	39	40
41	42	43	44	45	46	47	48	49	50
51	52	53	54	55	56	57	58	59	60

One More Than/Less Than
Ten More Than/Less Than

You can use a hundred chart to find a number that is 1 more than, 1 less than, 10 more than, or 10 less than a given number.

Find the number 42 on the chart.

To find 1 more than 42, move to the right 1 square. 43 is one more than 42.

To find 1 less than 42, move to the left 1 square. 41 is one less than 42.

To find 10 more than 42, move down 1 square. 52 is ten more than 42.

To find 10 less than 42, move up 1 square. 32 is ten less than 42.

Practice Finding More Than/Less Than a Number

Materials hundred chart

Have your child find the number 47 on the hundred chart. Have her or him use the chart to find 1 more, 1 less, 10 more, and 10 less than 47. Ask your child to explain how she or he found the answers.

Observe Your Child

As your child explains how he or she found the answers, encourage him or her to make generalizations about which directions to move on the chart to find numbers that are more and less. For example, "I move up or to the left to find numbers that are less."

Nombre _____

Entender el valor de posición

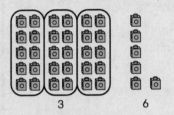

Se puede pensar en un número que está formado por decenas y unidades.
36 es igual que 3 grupos de 10 y 6 unidades.

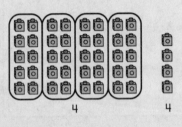

Se puede escribir un número observando los grupos de decenas y los sobrantes.
44 es igual que 4 grupos de 10 y 4 unidades.

Escribir números con grupos de 10

Materiales 30 monedas de 1¢ o fichas, papel y lápiz

Pida a su niño(a) que escoja un número entre 20 y 30. Pídale que cuente las monedas de 1¢ que equivalen a ese número. Luego pídale que agrupe las monedas de 1¢ en grupos de 10. Pídale que escriba el número de grupos de 10 y el número de unidades sobrantes. Repita la actividad con otro número.

Observe a su niño(a)

Señale objetos del entorno de su niño(a) y pídale que diga el número de decenas. Por ejemplo, señale los carros en un estacionamiento y pídale que diga cuántos grupos de 10 hay.

Name _____

Understand Place Value

Dear Family,

Your child is learning that two-digit numbers represent amounts of tens and ones. In this topic, he or she will learn to count two-digit numbers in groups of 10 with some ones left over. This will provide a foundation for future topics involving place value.

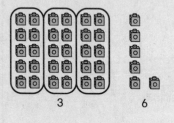

You can think of a number as being made up of tens and ones.
36 is the same as 3 groups of 10 and 6 ones.

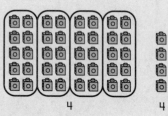

You can write a number by looking at the groups of tens and what is left over.
44 is the same as 4 groups of 10 and 4 ones.

Writing Numbers with Groups of 10

Materials 30 pennies or counters, paper and pencil

Have your child pick a number between 20 and 30. Have him or her count out pennies that equal that number. Then have your child group the pennies into groups of 10. Have your child write the number of groups of 10 and the number of ones left over. Repeat the activity with another number.

Observe Your Child

Point out objects in your child's environment and have him or her tell you the number of tens. For example, point out the cars in a parking lot and have your child tell you how many groups of 10 there are.

Ampliar la sucesión de conteo

Estimada familia:

En este tema, su niño(a) aprenderá estrategias para contar más de 100. Estas estrategias incluyen contar de 10 en 10, contar en una tabla numérica hasta 120 y contar hacia adelante en una recta numérica vacía.

Los siguientes ejemplos demuestran cómo contar hacia adelante de 1 en 1 y de 10 en 10 usando una parte de una tabla de 120.

Cuenta de 1 en 1 desde 102.
Fíjate en la misma fila. Muévete hacia la derecha 1 casilla cada vez.
102, 103, 104, 105

Cuenta de 10 en 10 desde 72.
Fíjate en la misma columna. Muévete hacia abajo 1 fila cada vez.
72, 82, 92, 102, 112

71	72	73	74	75	76	77	78	79	80
81	82	83	84	85	86	87	88	89	90
91	92	93	94	95	96	97	98	99	100
101	102	103	104	105	106	107	108	109	110
111	112	113	114	115	116	117	118	119	120

Usar la tabla de 120

Materiales tabla de 120, diferentes marcadores fluorescentes o crayones

Escoja un número de la tabla. Pida a su niño(a) que le diga qué número viene antes y qué número sigue después. Pídale que cuente de 1 en 1 hacia adelante hasta 5 números más. Escoja otro número y pídale que cuente de 10 en 10.

Observe a su niño(a)

Pídale que use un marcador fluorescente o un crayón de diferente color para colorear los números cada vez que él o ella cuenta de 10 en 10. Esto le facilitará analizar el patrón.

Extend the Counting Sequence

Dear Family,

In this topic, your child will learn strategies to count beyond 100. These strategies include counting by 10s, counting on a number chart to 120, and counting on an open number line.

The examples below demonstrate how to count forward by 1s and by 10s using part of a 120 chart.

Count by 1s from 102.
Look in the same row. Move to the right
1 square each time.
102, 103, 104, 105

71	72	73	74	75	76	77	78	79	80
81	82	83	84	85	86	87	88	89	90
91	92	93	94	95	96	97	98	99	100
101	102	103	104	105	106	107	108	109	110
111	112	113	114	115	116	117	118	119	120

Count by 10s from 72.
Look in the same column. Move down
1 row each time.
72, 82, 92, 102, 112

Using the 120 Chart

Materials 120 chart, different highlighters or crayons

Pick a number on the chart. Ask your child to tell you the number that comes before and the number that comes after. Have him or her count by 1s, going forward 5 numbers. Pick another number and have your child count by 10s.

Observe Your Child

Have him or her use a different-colored highlighter or crayon to shade the numbers each time he or she counts by 10s. This will make it easy to analyze the pattern.

Representar e interpretar datos

Estimada familia:

Su niño(a) está aprendiendo a organizar información en diferentes tipos de gráficas. En este tema, aprenderá a usar marcas de conteo y hacer pictografías.

Usar pictografías

Deportes favoritos

Esta es una pictografía sobre los deportes favoritos de los estudiantes. Se puede usar para responder preguntas como: ¿Cuántos estudiantes escogieron beisbol como su deporte favorito? Cuenten el número de pelotas de beisbol en la segunda fila. Hay 5 pelotas de beisbol, lo que significa que 5 estudiantes escogieron beisbol como su deporte favorito.

Usar pictografías

Materiales Papel y lápiz

Dibuje una pictografía sobre las comidas favoritas de su familia y trabaje con su niño(a) para completarla. Haga una pregunta a su niño(a) sobre la información de la gráfica. Pida a su niño(a) que explique cómo hallar la respuesta a la pregunta. Luego repita la actividad pidiendo a su niño(a) que le haga una pregunta sobre la gráfica.

Observe a su niño(a)

A medida que usted y su niño(a) se hacen preguntas, asegúrese de que él o ella usa términos matemáticos precisos, como *tabla de conteo y pictografía*.

Name _____

Represent and Interpret Data

Dear Family,

Your child is learning to organize information in different types of graphs. In this topic, he or she will learn to use tally marks and make picture graphs.

Using Picture Graphs

Favorite Sports

Soccer	⚽ ⚽ ⚽ ⚽ ⚽ ⚽ ⚽ ⚽ ⚽
Baseball	⚾ ⚾ ⚾ ⚾ ⚾
Basketball	🏀 🏀 🏀 🏀 🏀 🏀

This is a picture graph about the favorite sports of students. You can use it to answer questions such as this: How many students chose baseball as their favorite sport? Count the number of baseballs in the second row. There are 5 baseballs, which means 5 students chose baseball as their favorite sport.

Using Picture Graphs

Materials Paper and pencil

Draw a picture graph about your family's favorite meals and work with your child to complete it. Ask your child a question about the information in the graph. Have him or her explain how to find the answer to the question. Then repeat the activity by having your child ask you a question about the graph.

Observe Your Child

As you and your child ask each other questions, be sure your child is using precise mathematical terms, such as *tally chart* and *picture graph*.

Nombre _____

Trabajar con ecuaciones de suma y resta

Estimada familia:

Su niño(a) está aprendiendo a trabajar con ecuaciones de suma y resta. En este tema, aprenderá estrategias para resolver problemas verbales de varios pasos y problemas con tres sumandos. Su niño(a) también aprenderá a hallar números desconocidos, o que faltan, en una ecuación. El siguiente ejemplo muestra cómo hallar un número que falta para hacer que una ecuación sea verdadera.

Hallar los números que faltan para hacer que una ecuación sea verdadera

Completa el número que falta que hace que la ecuación sea verdadera.

$12 - \underline{\hspace{1cm}} = 5 + 3$

Paso 1 Resuelve la parte de la ecuación que no tiene el número desconocido.
$5 + 3 = 8$

Paso 2 Vuelve a escribir la ecuación con este total.
$12 - \underline{\hspace{1cm}} = 8$

Paso 3 Puedes usar fichas para resolver la ecuación.
$12 - \underline{\hspace{1cm}} = 8$

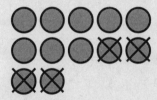

Por tanto, $12 - 4 = 5 + 3$.

Hallar el número que falta

Materiales papel; lápiz; frijoles, clips u otros objetos pequeños

Escriba una ecuación que incluya un número que falta. Por ejemplo: $11 + \underline{\hspace{1cm}} = 18$. Pida a su niño(a) que muestre cómo se resuelve la ecuación usando objetos pequeños. Repita con una ecuación que tenga expresiones en ambos lados del signo igual, como la que se muestra en el ejemplo de arriba.

Observe a su niño(a)

Escriba la siguiente ecuación incorrecta: $5 + 4 = 14 - 6$. Pida a su niño(a) que explique por qué la ecuación no es verdadera. Permítale que use objetos pequeños para explicar su razonamiento si es necesario.

Name _____

Work with Addition and Subtraction Equations

Dear Family,

Your child is learning to work with addition and subtraction equations. In this topic, he or she will learn strategies to solve multistep word problems and problems with three addends. Your child will also learn to find unknown, or missing, numbers in an equation. The following example shows how to find a missing number to make an equation true.

Find Missing Numbers to Make a True Equation

Fill in the missing number that makes the equation true.

$$12 - \underline{\hspace{1cm}} = 5 + 3$$

Step 1 Solve the side of the equation without the unknown number.

$$5 + 3 = 8$$

Step 2 Rewrite the equation with this sum.

$$12 - \underline{\hspace{1cm}} = 8$$

Step 3 You can use counters to solve the equation.

$$12 - \underline{\hspace{1cm}} = 8$$

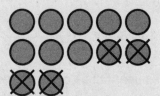

So, $12 - 4 = 5 + 3$.

Find the Missing Number

Materials paper; pencil; beans, paper clips, or other small objects

Write an equation that includes a missing number. For example, $11 + \underline{\hspace{1cm}} = 18$. Have your child model solving the equation using small objects. Repeat this with an equation that has expressions on both sides of the equal sign, such as the one modeled in the example above.

Observe Your Child

Write the following incorrect equation: $5 + 4 = 14 - 6$. Have your child explain why the equation is not true. Allow him or her to use small objects, if needed, to explain his or her reasoning.

Nombre _____

Operaciones de resta hasta 20: Usar estrategias

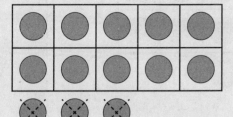
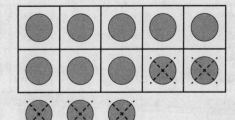
Forma 10 para restar

Materiales Monedas de un centavo, tarjetas de fichero, bolsas de papel, papel, lápiz

Dibuje un marco de diez en un papel. Escriba los números 11 a 15 en un conjunto de tarjetas de fichero y 6 a 10 en otro conjunto. Ponga cada conjunto de tarjetas de fichero en una bolsa de papel. Pida a su niño(a) que escoja un número de cada bolsa.

Pida a su niño(a) que escriba una ecuación de resta usando un número de la primera bolsa y luego un número de la segunda bolsa. Pida a su niño(a) que resuelva el problema con un marco de diez y monedas de un centavo.

Observe a su niño(a)

Comente cómo los marcos de diez y las monedas de un centavo fueron buenas herramientas para resolver el problema anterior.

Name _____

Subtraction Facts to 20: Use Strategies

Dear Family,

Your child is learning to use different strategies to solve subtraction facts to 20. One of the strategies your child will use is Make 10 to Subtract. This strategy helps break a subtraction problem into two simpler problems. The subtraction strategies in this topic will also help your child communicate mathematical ideas and solve word problems.

Make 10 to Subtract

You can make 10 to help find $13 - 5$.
First subtract 3 to make 10.
$13 - 3 = 10$

Then subtract 2 more because $3 + 2 = 5$.
You need to subtract 5 altogether.

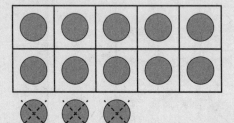

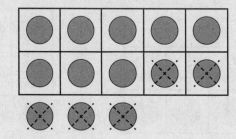

$$10 - 2 = 8$$
$$So, 13 - 5 = 8.$$

Make 10 to Subtract

Materials Pennies, index cards, paper bags, paper and pencil

Draw a blank ten-frame on paper. Write the numbers 11–15 on one set of index cards and 6–10 on another set. Place each set of cards in a paper bag. Have your child choose one number from each bag.

Have your child write a subtraction equation using a number from the first bag and then a number from the second bag. Have him or her solve the problem with the ten-frame and pennies.

Observe Your Child

Discuss how the ten-frames and the pennies were good tools to help solve the problem above.

Nombre _____

Operaciones de suma hasta 20: Usar estrategias

Estimada familia:

Su niño(a) está aprendiendo sobre el uso de las estrategias para sumar hasta 20. En este tema, él o ella aprenderá varias estrategias para hallar sumas. Entre estas estrategias están contar hacia adelante, formar diez, hacer dobles y sumar 1 o 2 a los dobles. Se puede usar una recta numérica vacía para contar hacia adelante. Su niño(a) cuenta hacia adelante "saltando" en la recta numérica.

Por ejemplo, la siguiente recta numérica muestra cómo resolver 7 + 8. Si se empieza en 7 y se dan 8 saltos a la derecha, se llega al 15. Por tanto, 7 + 8 = 15.

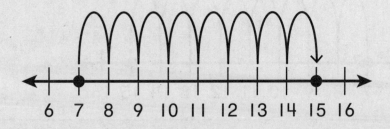

Contar hacia adelante para sumar

Materiales papel, lápiz

Dibuje una recta numérica que muestre los números del 1 al 20. Escriba la siguiente ecuación en un papel: 6 + 8 = ?. Demuestre cómo contar hacia adelante usando la recta numérica empezando en 6 y saltando 8 veces hacia la derecha. Pregunte a su niño(a): "¿A qué número llegué?". Repita el ejercicio usando el siguiente problema: 7 + 6. Esta vez, pida a su niño(a) que practique el conteo hacia adelante usando la recta numérica.

Observe a su niño(a)

Escriba la siguiente ecuación en el papel: 6 + 6 = 14. Pregunte a su niño(a) si está de acuerdo con su respuesta. Pida a su niño(a) que use una recta numérica para resolver el problema y determinar si la ecuación es correcta o incorrecta.

Addition Facts to 20: Use Strategies

Dear Family,

Your child is learning about strategies to use to add to 20. In this topic, he or she will learn several strategies for finding sums. Some of the strategies include counting on, making ten, making doubles, and adding 1 or 2 to doubles. An open number line can be used to count on. Your child counts on by "hopping" up the number line.

For example, the number line below shows how to solve $7 + 8$. If you start at 7 and hop 8 times to the right, you land on 15. So, $7 + 8 = 15$.

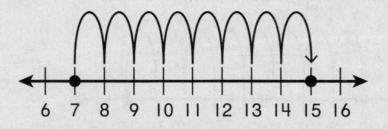

Counting On to Add

Materials paper, pencil

Draw a number line showing numerals 1–20. Write the following equation on the paper: $6 + 8 = ?$. Demonstrate how to count on using the number line by starting at 6 and hopping 8 times to the right. Ask your child: "What number did I land on?" Repeat the exercise using the following problem: $7 + 6$. This time, have your child practice counting on using the number line.

Observe Your Child

Write the following equation on the paper: $6 + 6 = 14$. Ask your child if he or she agrees with your answer. Have your child use a number line to solve the problem and determine whether your equation is correct or incorrect.

Sumar y restar con facilidad hasta 10

Estimada familia:

Su niño(a) está aprendiendo a sumar y restar usando números hasta 10. En este tema, su niño(a) aprenderá a contar hacia adelante para resolver problemas de suma y hacia atrás para resolver problemas de resta. Su niño(a) también aprenderá sobre la relación entre suma y resta.

Contar hacia adelante para sumar

Paty pone 4 papas en una olla y luego añade 2 papas más. ¿Cuántas papas hay ahora en la olla?

4 + 2 = ___6___

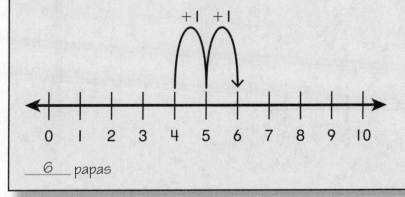

___6___ papas

Contar hacia adelante para sumar

Materiales 10 objetos pequeños, papel, lápiz

Ponga entre 1 y 7 objetos pequeños sobre una mesa y pida a su niño(a) que cuente los objetos. Luego ponga 1, 2 o 3 objetos más sobre la mesa y pida a su niño(a) que cuente hacia adelante para hallar el número total de objetos sobre la mesa. Después pida a su niño(a) que practique ecuaciones de suma que correspondan al número de objetos sobre la mesa.

Observe a su niño(a)

Incluya una recta numérica con la actividad anterior. Pida a su niño(a) que resuelva ecuaciones usando la recta numérica.

Fluently Add and Subtract Within 10

Count On to Add

Pat puts 4 potatoes in a pot. Then he adds 2 more potatoes to the pot. How many potatoes are in the pot now?

$4 + 2 = \underline{\quad 6 \quad}$

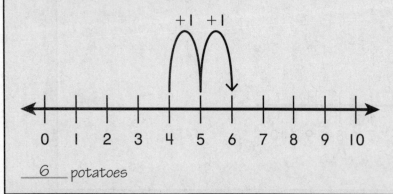

$\underline{\quad 6 \quad}$ potatoes

Count On to Add

Materials 10 small objects, paper, pencil

Place between 1 and 7 small objects on a table. Have your child count the objects. Then place another 1, 2, or 3 objects on the table. Have your child count on to find the total number of objects on the table. Then have him or her practice writing addition equations that correspond to the number of objects on the table.

Observe Your Child

Include a number line with the previous activity. Have your child solve the equations using the number line.

Nombre _____

La suma y la resta

Estimada familia:

Su niño(a) está aprendiendo a sumar y restar. En este tema aprenderá a resolver problemas sumando o restando y a escribir ecuaciones de suma y resta. Estas son destrezas básicas importantes que le permitirán a su niño(a) comunicar ideas y razonamientos matemáticos. Estas destrezas también le permitirán analizar la información dada en problemas verbales y hallar soluciones. Aprenderá cómo usar modelos para resolver problemas verbales.

Cada lado del tablero representa las partes de un todo. El número en el recuadro de arriba representa el total. El modelo se puede completar con la información que se da en un problema verbal. Cuando falta una de las partes, se escribe una ecuación de resta o una ecuación con un sumando desconocido. Cuando falte el total, se escribe una ecuación de suma.

Escribir ecuaciones de suma

Materiales 8 objetos pequeños, papel, lápiz

Tome 5 objetos pequeños, como clips o botones, y divídalos en 2 grupos. Pida a su niño(a) que escriba 2 ecuaciones de suma para los objetos. Después pida a su niño(a) que divida los objetos en 2 grupos diferentes. Escriba 2 ecuaciones de suma para los objetos y pida a su niño(a) que le ayude a decidir si están correctas. Repita la actividad con 6 y 8 objetos.

Observe a su niño(a)

Comenten cómo es que los objetos son buenas herramientas para representar las ecuaciones. Luego, comenten otras maneras para representar las ecuaciones.

Name _____

Understand Addition and Subtraction

Dear Family,

Your child is learning about addition and subtraction. In this topic, your child will learn to solve problems by adding or subtracting and writing addition and subtraction equations. These are important foundational skills that will allow your child to communicate mathematical ideas and reasoning. These skills will also allow your child to analyze the information given in word problems and find solutions. Your child will learn how to use models to solve word problems.

Each side of the mat represents parts of a whole. The number in the box above the mat represents the total. You can complete the model based on information given in a word problem. When one of the parts is missing, write a subtraction equation or an equation with an unknown addend. When the total is missing, write an addition equation.

Writing Addition Equations

Materials 8 small objects, paper, pencil

Take 5 small objects, such as paper clips or buttons, and divide them into 2 groups. Have your child write 2 addition equations for the objects. Then allow your child to divide the objects into 2 different groups. Write 2 addition equations for the objects and have your child help you decide if they are correct. Repeat the activity with 6 and 8 objects.

Observe Your Child

Discuss how the objects are good tools to model the equations. Then discuss other ways to model the equations.

Home-School Connection

Topics 1–15

Nombre _____

Razonar usando figuras y sus atributos

Estimada familia:

Su niño(a) está aprendiendo sobre geometría. En este tema, él o ella aprenderá a identificar figuras bidimensonales y tridimensionales a partir de sus atributos y a combinar figuras para formar nuevas figuras.

Identificar atributos de figuras tridimensionales

La siguiente figura tridimensional es un prisma rectangular.

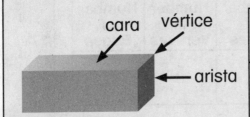

Figura	Número de caras	Número de vértices	Número de aristas
Prisma rectangular	6	8	12

Contar caras, vértices y aristas

Materiales Objetos del hogar que sean figuras tridimensionales (lata de sopa, caja de zapatos, pelota de playa, etc.), papel, lápiz

Escoja un objeto del hogar que sea una figura tridimensional. Dígale a su niño(a) que nombre la figura. Luego, haga una tabla como la que se muestra arriba y añada el nombre de la figura a la tabla. Pídale a su niño(a) que cuente el número de caras, o superficies planas, el número de vértices y el número de aristas. Añada esta información a la tabla y repita el proceso con otros objetos del hogar.

Observe a su niño(a)

A medida que su niño(a) observa figuras bidimensionales y tridimensionales, pídale que explique cómo se identifica una figura dada. Por ejemplo, su niño(a) podría identificar que un cono tiene 1 superficie plana y 1 vértice y puede rodar.

Name _____

Reason with Shapes and Their Attributes

Dear Family,

Your child is beginning to learn about geometry. In this topic, he or she will learn to identify two-dimensional and three-dimensional shapes based on their attributes and to combine shapes to form new shapes.

Identifying Attributes of Three-Dimensional Shapes

The three-dimensional shape shown below is a rectangular prism.

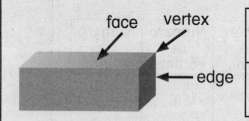
face   vertex
edge

Shape	Number of Faces	Number of Vertices	Number of Edges
Rectangular Prism	6	8	12

Counting Faces, Vertices, and Edges

Materials Household objects that have three-dimensional shapes (soup can, shoebox, beach ball, etc.), paper, pencil

Choose a household object that has a three-dimensional shape. Ask your child to name the shape. Then make a table like the one shown above and add the name of the shape to the table. Have your child count the number of faces or flat surfaces, the number of vertices, and the number of edges. Add this information to the table and repeat the process with other household objects.

Observe Your Child

As your child looks at two-dimensional and three-dimensional shapes, ask him or her to explain how to identify a given shape. For example, your child might recognize that a cone has 1 flat surface and 1 vertex, and can roll.

Name _____

Equal Shares of Circles and Rectangles

Dear Family,

Your child is learning about fractional portions of geometric shapes. In this topic, he or she will learn to make and describe equal shares, such as halves and fourths, of whole objects. This understanding will provide foundational knowledge for fraction concepts in later grades.

This circle is divided into 2 equal shares. It is divided into halves.

This rectangle is divided into 4 equal shares. It is divided into fourths or quarters.

Making Equal Shares

Materials paper, scissors, crayons

Work with your child to cut out several paper squares, circles, and rectangles. Ask your child to choose a shape and to use a crayon to divide the shape into 2 equal shares. Ask if there is a different way to divide the shape into 2 equal shares. Repeat the process with a different shape. Then repeat the process by asking your child to divide the shape into 4 equal shares. In each case, encourage your child to consider different ways to divide the shape into the required number of equal shares.

Observe Your Child

Work with your child to cut out two identical copies of a shape. Have him or her divide one of the shapes into 2 equal shares and divide the other into 4 equal shares. Ask your child to explain which of the two shapes is divided into a greater number of equal shares. Then have him or her explain which shape has larger equal shares. Your child can answer these questions by comparing the shapes side by side or by reasoning about the quantities involved.

Nombre _____

Partes iguales de círculos y rectángulos

Estimada familia:

Su niño(a) está aprendiendo sobre las partes fraccionarias de figuras geométricas. En este tema, aprenderá a formar y describir partes iguales, como mitades y cuartos, de objetos enteros. Esta comprensión será un conocimiento básico para los temas que siguen sobre fracciones.

Este círculo está dividido en 2 partes iguales. Está dividido en mitades.

Este rectángulo está dividido en 4 partes iguales. Está dividido en cuartos.

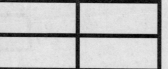

Formar partes iguales

Materiales papel, tijeras, crayones

Trabaje con su niño(a) para recortar varios cuadrados, círculos y rectángulos de papel. Pídale que escoja una figura y que use un crayón para dividir la figura en 2 partes iguales. Pregúntele si hay una manera diferente de dividir la figura en 2 partes iguales. Repita el proceso con una figura diferente. Luego, repita el proceso pidiéndole a su niño(a) que divida la figura en 4 partes iguales. En cada caso, anímelo(a) a pensar en diferentes maneras de dividir la figura en el número requerido de partes iguales.

Observe a su niño(a)

Trabaje con su niño(a) para recortar dos copias idénticas de una figura. Pídale que divida una de las figuras en 2 partes iguales y que divida la otra en 4 partes iguales. Pídale que explique cuál de las dos figuras está dividida en un número mayor de partes iguales. Luego, pídale que explique qué figura tiene partes iguales más grandes. Su niño(a) puede responder estas preguntas comparando las figuras una junto a la otra, o razonando sobre las cantidades involucradas.